Suffolk

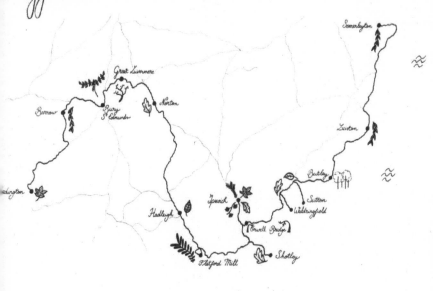

AN ANTHOLOGY

Suffolk Arboretum

East Anglian stories
inspired by remarkable trees

Foreword by Tom Brown
of The Light Green Trust

First edition 2022

Cover design and formatting www.jdsmith-design.com

Published by University of Suffolk

https://www.uos.ac.uk/courses/pg/ma-creative-and-critical-writing

Printed and bound in Great Britain
by Clays Ltd, Elcograf S.p.A

ISBN: 978-1-9989996-3-7

For Antonella Castelvedere

With love, always.

Welcome to our anthology *Suffolk Arboretum*. This is the second collection of original stories from the Creative and Critical Writing postgraduates at the University of Suffolk. Following on from the much-loved *Suffolk Folk* anthology which looked at folk tales of the region, this anthology turns its attention to the remarkable woodland and trees of Suffolk. Our anthology theme this year coincides with the Queen's Platinum Jubilee and the national Green Canopy Initiative. At the University of Suffolk, while the MA Creative and Critical Writing students were exploring our county and choosing remarkable trees to write about, our Chancellor Professor Helen Pankhurst and our Vice-Chancellor Helen Langton, were planting fruit trees on campus. Seven trees to represent each decade of Her Majesty's reign. These include the rare nineteenth century apple *Edmund Pippin*, an ancient quince, an Edwardian variety of plum called J*ubilee* and a *May Duke* cherry tree which dates back to the eighteenth century. It's good to think that in years to come, their harvests will be enjoyed by staff and students as well as the birds and insects who will also come in search of sweetness and shelter.

It is possible to find every tree or area of woodland that is featured in these stories. We recommend you take a tour of Suffolk with the anthology in hand and find each tree, from Haverhill to Lowestoft. Sit in their dappled shade and read the original writing that they inspired.

As an addition to the anthology, we have also included in this book, the winning and shortlisted entries from the Student New Angle Prize Writing Awards 2022. This award is offered by the Ipswich Institute which runs the national New Angle Prize for Literature. Both competitions celebrate writing that evokes the rich and varied cultural landscapes of East Anglia.

We would like to thank Jane Dixon Smith for her help with the beautiful cover design and everybody who worked on and inspired this collection. Thank you to Natasha O'Brien for all her hard work in helping to edit and collate the anthology and thank you to Amber Spalding and Alison Dudeney for their work on our podcast show. https://anchor.fm/university-of-suffolk

Suffolk Arboretum is dedicated to Dr Antonella Castelvedere, a cherished friend, colleague, and influential educator. In loving memory of her inspiring ways, her brilliance and her generosity of heart and mind.

Dr Amanda Hodgkinson
Associate Professor English and Creative Writing
University of Suffolk 2022

Foreword by Tom Brown CEO of The Green Light Trust.

My career and life to date have been shaped by Suffolk and its trees, so it is a privilege to be asked to write the forward to this anthology inspired by remarkable trees and woodland.

Trees and our innate connection to woodlands are something that has fascinated me for much of my adult life. After an early and incredibly unfulfilling job in corporate sales, I fell into working for a tree surgeon. The money was awful, but I felt at home in my surroundings in a way I hadn't experienced in work before. This almost counteracted the feeling of complete exhaustion at the end of each day. I didn't know why I felt so at ease at the time, but I do now. It is undeniable that as humans we have evolved to exist in green spaces and around trees. For example, the human eye can see more shades of green than any other colour. For this very reason, we find it easier to "just be" when we are surrounded by trees and plants. Our brains don't need to work as hard to process and be in these environments. Trees, like us, are influenced by their environments if you have ever seen a tree growing at a strange angle as it struggles to reach the light you will have observed this in action. Interestingly, this tree is being pushed away from the dark as a plant hormone called *Auxin* gathers on the dark side of the stem lengthening the cells in the stem on that side pushing it away from the dark and reaching towards the light. Evolution has driven amazing adaptations in trees, like mangroves that thrive in the most inhospitably salty conditions. But if their environments change too fast evolution can't keep up and tree species die. So, what have mangroves got to do with Suffolk? Well, much like mangrove tree species would struggle to adapt to living in Suffolk, as people, we struggle to live in the rapidly changing world moving us away from trees and nature.

Suffolk has some truly amazing trees and woodlands from large forests like those in Rendlesham famous for its extra-terrestrial links, nationally significant ancient woodlands like Bradfield and Frithy in the West and individually important and veteran trees in its historic landscape and many arboretums. Trees and woodlands are a quintessential part of what makes Suffolk, Suffolk. Even our county flower the Oxlip is a graceful woodland dweller. Suffolk quite literally has an abundance of nature; I believe it is one of the county's greatest untapped assets.

As CEO of The Green Light Trust, a charity which beliefs in the power of nature. I see the influence that engaging with nature and woodlands can have on our lives. Both physical and mental health can be positively influenced by our connection and access to this resource. It has been proven that significant health indicators such as birth weight, cortisol levels, dietary choices, exercise habits, longevity and quality of life can be impacted by our engagement and access to high-quality doses of nature. I am fascinated by the fact that just seeing nature in a hospital can significantly speed up a patient's recovery. Ten years ago, I listened transfixed as Matilda Van Den Bosch a research scientist described her studies using VR headsets to control the dose and the impact it had on the subjects.

So why then do I describe this resource as untapped? Sadly, access to nature is also an indicator of inequalities in society. For example, tree canopy coverage is measured by identifying how much of an area is blocked out by the leafy areas of the trees. The higher the number the greater the number of trees. Many large metropolitan areas have been surveyed and it is always the most affluent areas that have the greatest canopy coverage. It isn't just socioeconomic standing that influences access to nature. In 2020 Friends of the Earth published research on green space deprivation. This can be broadly described as not living within ten minutes of high-quality green space such as a park. In the UK if you are black or from a minority ethnic background, you are over three times more likely to live in a green space deprived area than white people. Indirect health factors can also be affected by trees. Climate change is driving extremes of weather including higher temperatures for prolonged periods. Living in streets with trees has a significant cooling effect reducing the impact of these temperature spikes.

At The Green Light Trust, we harness the power of nature to support the most vulnerable, marginalised and often ignored or disregarded in society. We work with people of all ages who are recovering from and facing a multitude of challenges in their lives. Such as poor mental health, substance misuse, offending behaviours, additional learning needs, poor educational attainment, and many others. The common thread in almost all of their lives is that they have stalled for one reason or another. I am often struck by the stories of the people we work with and can see how many of us are just a few bad decisions or unfortunate events away from being in the same position.

For the people we support, nature and woodlands aren't a magic cure like some kind of anointed profit laying their healing hands on someone. But the acceptance, belonging and time we can give the thousands of people we support each year, delivered in an environment where they feel the belonging that I felt when I started climbing trees for a living, is as close to a cure as we can get.

Over time the people we support begin to associate engaging with nature and the woodlands we deliver our support from, as positive for their health. This is something they can take with them for the rest of their lives. I believe access to nature and woodlands is about more than just our proximity to it. If you have never grown up knowing for example, how to identify the difference between the trees described so beautifully in this anthology or have had the chance to feel the calming and cooling embrace of the shade of a mighty Oak on a sunny day, even if it is right there you won't engage with it.

Amongst many the good habits, we help people to form very subtly through our programmes bridging this gap is one of the most enduring. We work in partnership with organisations such as The National Trust and The RSPB to help them broaden access to their sites and better include the people we support. I believe this gives even greater value to Suffolk's trees and woodlands. Just through reductions in GP and A&E visits and police interactions alone we save the taxpayer more than £1000 per adult we support in the first year of their support alone. Many of the people we support go back to work, indeed about 10-15% of our paid staff are individuals who have been through our support and trained. If you add the contribution of these changes in their lives this figure can rise to almost a £15,000 contribution in year one and up to £25,000 after ten years. Scale that up across the people we support and the woodlands we work in are pretty valuable to Suffolk.

When you read this anthology think about the untapped value of the trees and woodlands described across our green and pleasant county, and hopefully you too will start to think about how we can tap into that value. Even if all you do is take the time to appreciate just how awesome trees are!

Contents

WEST SUFFOLK

The Kedington Horse Chestnut by Dinah Cowan

The horse chestnut of this story can be found in Silver Street Park, Kedington, Suffolk, on the bank of the Stour, to the left of the bridge that traverses the river. I was certain that I wasn't going to choose an ancient yew or an imposing oak for my piece for this book – not a tree of noteworthy importance. I wanted to explore the notion that even trees of little historical or botanical significance are still so vital – would also have witnessed much over their lifetimes, have their own stories to tell, and are of importance from an eco-critical perspective and post-humanist considerations of non-human relationality. I was keen to write a piece that echoed my love for both stories and the natural world.

I hadn't originally planned to write about a felled tree; it is thanks to my mother-in-law for sowing that particular seed. I have family in Kedington, and often walk my in-law's dog, Amber, through Silver Street Park after our run around The Great Meadow. And so it was that following my mother-in-law's suggestion one crisp Sunday in January 2022, Amber and I went for a closer look at the horse chestnut of this story.

I was struck by the sadness I felt for it having been felled in the first place, but I was pleased that it had been left, supporting life in death. I hope that if you visit, you too will spot a spider's web, will run your fingertips across the fissured bark, imagine a carved love heart, and what became of those who played, courted, sheltered at the feet of this horse chestnut tree, imagine all that she witnessed. I hope that you look up at the trees to her left, to her right.

A Life through the Seasons by Dinah Cowan

Autumn, 1860

A squirrel scrapes a hole in the soft, warm earth, buries its
treasure. It won't return for it. It's been a bountiful season;
there will be ample nuts to sustain it through the winter,
there will be no need to resort to the bitterness of a conker.

Winter, 1909

The conditions had proved perfect. Abandoned by the
squirrel, you had rested, dormant through those winter
months, until frost and rain softened your hard coat and
your embryonic growth had pushed upwards, seeking sun,
nutrients, life.

Now, you are tall, and winter-bare, starkly profiled
against a bleached and leaden sky, outstretched branches
like a milkmaid's yoke, balancing the snowdrifts that curve
fatly towards your trunk. Evocative of a Grimms' fairy-tale,
the sticky buds embellishing the tips of your twigs are
blood-red against the white of the landscape.

All is still now, all is silent. Unnaturally so. The tempest
had ravaged and tormented the county until dawn, and the
ensuant calm is that of a stunned land waiting to catch its

breath. The ambient sounds of village life are absorbed by a thick blanket of snow and a few feet from your roots, the River Stour is muted beneath a layer of opaque ice. A family of mallards squat patiently on the bank, awaiting the thaw, feet tucked tightly under warm down.

The spell is broken by a huddle of boys coming onto the meadow, scurrying across the short bridge that traverses the Stour. They are animated, exchanging raillery, egging each other on to try out another, more dangerous skid, although their hobnailed boots keep them disappointingly safe. Beneath their caps their eyes are darting, shiny with excitement and disobedience; they had each been sternly warned by their mothers to stay indoors, to wait until after church. But temptation had proved too much, and it took just one, he on the slackest rein and loosest knot of the apron strings, to muster his friends.

They reach you quickly, bend to plunge woollen-gloved hands into the pristine snow. The missiles are launched chiefly at each other, but one off-target shot knocks the snow from a branch; there is an alluring spray and satisfying dull thud as it lands, and so you have their attention now. Snowballs pound your trunk, stick wetly to bark still the pinky-grey of youth. Your twigs quiver, and one boy jumps for a lower stem, hanging there, legs swinging for a triumphant second or two before it snaps. He brushes off his friends' jeers along with the snow from his backside, as the bells of St Peter and St Paul - visible from your upper branches - begin to toll. The boys hurry away, to face their mothers' wrath, and their God.

But the one who damaged you pulls up, lets his friends depart without him. He trudges back to you, looks up at your injury. Your broken stem hangs ragged, an oblique fracture, bark peeled back high above the wound. Only last summer, he had stood here with his youngest sister, had shown her the bees, hard at work among your flowers. *Busy bees, busy bees*, she had sung on the way home, atop his shoulders. And here, with his father, just a few months ago, collecting your conkers. His father, who would be cross – no, worse disappointed - if he knew. Guilt and shame nudge at the edges of the boy's consciousness, taint the pleasures of the morning. He trails his fingertips across your trunk, mouths *sorry*.

The evergreen trees to your left and right watch on, sheltering you.

Summer, 1945

It's show time. You are abundantly in leaf, your branches hanging with candelabras of flowers, fat pyramidal inflorescences that on close inspection resemble a troupe of ballerinas – white dresses with splashes of yellow, salmon pink or carmine at the waist, pistils en-pointe. Bees perform their own aerobatic ballet, dancing from flower to flower to collect your precious nectar. Your leaves have another visitor, attracting the attention of a hungry blue tit, which swoops and rises with a caterpillar of the leaf-miner moth flailing in its beak.

A young couple stroll across the meadow, holding hands, pause beside you as he finishes regaling her with a humorous story to which she has been listening with the beatific smile of the newly smitten. A squirrel, alerted, scurries up into your canopy as the man removes his battledress jacket, lays it upon the grass with a flourish, and the couple sit, reclined against your trunk. Your palmate leaves flutter above their heads like soothing hands as they chatter, heads inclined towards each other, their breaths that rise in the hot, still air mingling with the atmospheric gases, exchanged by you for the air that they breathe.

'My father used to play here,' the man says. 'Snowball fights in winter, picnics and the like in summer. It's like our family tree.'

They both laugh at the pun, and then she watches as he stands, removes a penknife from his pocket, winks at her. He begins to carve into your trunk, clumsy and faltering at first, before the correct pressure and angle is determined. Your bark is more mature now, has darkened, hardened, developed fissures that criss-cross and entwine, and as his knife slices, deeply, slivers of your skin slip to the ground. He forms an untidy heart, adds two sets of initials, *AS* and *RG*, beams at the woman as she flings her arms around him, offers up her mouth. Shortly afterwards, they gather the jacket, walk away.

The trees to your left and right take note, emit sugars from their roots to yours.

Autumn, 1981

The air is pungent with nature's turning, base notes of decay and rotting, the perfume that can render adults dizzy with nostalgia and longing for new pencils and notebooks, for shiny new shoes, pumpkin soup and apple pie studded with cloves. Your leaves are beginning to curl, are fringed in copper hues, twigs laden with twin sets of green conker shells, splitting open to reveal the seed within, the slit of an alien's eye.

A family enters the meadow – a mother with two children of junior school age and a toddler, who kicks her yellow wellington boots through the piles of crisp leaves, clapping her hands in delight at the birds who rise from your canopy in urgent, synchronised flight. She homes in on the puddles pocketing the sloping bank of the Stour, stamps with relish, muddy water splashing up onto her dungarees. Autumn: a wondrous season for a toddler.

The mother lays a blanket a few feet from you, opens a picnic basket, hands out sandwiches and pork pies, pours orange squash. Her children are impatient to begin their mission, however, and quickly abandon lunch to circle the leaf fall at your feet, gathering your fallen conkers, reaching up to pluck the green husks still clinging to your lower stems, exclaiming in surprise as the prickles stab vulnerable fingertips. The cases are prised open to reveal the cream fleshy inner, and ah, there it is, the glossy, rich mahogany marvel within. They savour the feel of these treasures, luxuriously silky smooth against their soft palms, before filling their anorak pockets until they bulge.

Gathering bread crusts for the ducks, the mother is distracted suddenly, approaches you, runs her fingertips across a ragged heart-shaped scar in the dark scaly plates of your bark. *AS* and *RG* she mouths silently. A frown ghosts across her brow, a memory itches to break free. *AS*, her paternal grandfather's initials – and wasn't there some tale, buried deep in the family lore, about a proposal under a tree? But her grandmother's name is Charlotte, her maiden name Clarke. She shakes her head, it doesn't matter, she is saddened by this cutting of you, whoever the perpetrator was. It's futile, this attempt to cover the carving, but she flattens her palm over it nonetheless, pictures it gone.

Do you feel her stroke, long after she has walked away, long after the children's laughter could be heard from the bridge as they competed in a game of pooh sticks, using the twigs they had harvested from the leaf mulch at your feet?

The trees to your left and right curve their roots towards yours.

Spring, 2011

The meadow is now a park, tamed, a tarmacked path circling its perimeter, a bandstand at its centre. Today, the annual charity duck race is in full swing - six hundred plastic yellow ducks bobbing and floating their way down the Stour to excited cheers from the crowds of onlookers. Chatter and laughter fill the air, the smell of barbecue from nearby Great Meadow floats on the breeze. Silver Street Bridge provides an ideal viewing point, and families gather beside you to watch the progress of the race, scanning the river for their own duck.

No-one pays you any attention.

If they did, they would notice the exposed and disc-oloured wood where your bark has fallen in places. They would see that your crown is thinning, might ponder why so few flowers have bloomed this year. They would surely not fail to see the cracks in your bark that are oozing a reddish-brown sticky liquid, tears of blood running down your trunk.

You are sick.

Bacteria have entered your skin, multiplied, blocked your water systems, your ability to drink. The trees to your left and right are now powerless to help.

You are dying.

Winter, 2022

I crouch beside you, let the dog sniff enthusiastically around the three sections of your trunk that have been left where you were felled. My fingertips travel along the fissures and crevices of your dehydrated bark, wrinkled by time and sunrays, the face of an old salt. I expect you could tell a few stories too – of those who sought shelter, courted, played at your feet.

You were probably never of noteworthy importance, I think. Not an imposing oak or a yew already ancient at the birth of Christianity. St Peter and St Paul stood in place hundreds of years before you germinated, grew tall enough to see it, when you were rooted and upright and beautiful.

My fingertips caress a scar in your bark that was not cast by nature's hand – a heart, looping two sets of initials, *AS* and *RG*. A love heart, but no act of love for you. Perhaps they didn't realise. I hope not. Theirs was never a story of noteworthy importance either, but it would have been to them, to those they loved, were loved by. I wonder what became of them.

From the earth clustered around one log, new growth has emerged, an evergreen, its species unknown to me. A spider's web glistens across the entrance to your hollow middle stump, a silken portcullis. Even in death, you are supporting life. I am glad they left you here, where you fell. I sit on one of your logs, look up at the trees to your left, to your right.

We feel your loss.

The Weeping Willow in Barrow by Sarah Clark

The only pub in England named after a weeping willow is in Barrow, Suffolk, a village eight miles west of Bury St Edmunds. Next to the pub, which has been there in some form since the 16th century, is a weeping willow tree. This tree may have been there just as long. During the 16th and 17th centuries, willow trees were sometimes associated with the grief of forsaken lovers. With this theme in mind, I researched Barrow and discovered Mary Beale, the renowned 17th century artist around whom I weaved my tale.

The Rector's Daughter by Sarah Clark

May 1648

Mary sat under the weeping willow tree next to the alehouse. Her father, the local rector, had bought her some new pencils from Borrowdale for her birthday, and after finishing her chores, she'd headed into the village to sit under her tree and draw while she waited for Richard. Her heart raced - just as it ached on the days when she didn't see him.

She loved the willow tree; it felt like the perfect place to draw and contemplate the world. If she sat to the rear of the tree, she could hide behind its verdant branches, which extended across the grass and almost reached to the ground in front of her. If she sat in front of it, she could look out across the dirt track road that led to Bury St Edmunds.

Some days, she watched and overheard travelling merchants and men from the village passing by and stopping at the alehouse. Her father always said that gossip was a woman's pastime but listening to these men would certainly prove him wrong.

She leaned against the trunk and studied her surroundings from beneath the willow's lazy, drooping boughs. It was almost summer, and the fat catkins of spring had dropped and given way to luxuriant leaves. She laid back against the tree, her eyes closed, absent-mindedly holding her pencil as she daydreamed of Richard.

Here, under this tree, was where she had been sitting when she'd laid eyes on him for the first time.

Mary met Richard one day in May, when he arrived at the alehouse with a group of friends, causing a commotion with their laughing and merrymaking. A boy of seventeen years or so, he'd caught her eye as she looked up from where she sat in front of the tree. Then, he changed direction to walk towards her. She'd looked quickly back to her drawing as he advanced. Mary did not want to invite interruption; she'd been trying to draw a snail that was stuck on a gnarled piece of tree root and was concentrating intently on the slow-moving creature.

'Good afternoon, Miss,' Richard said, in a gently mocking tone, pulling the branches to one side for a better view. 'And who do we have here?' He poked his tongue out - then she realized he was imitating her own expression of concentration. Embarrassed, she flushed and covered her mouth. When she looked up again, he was smiling.

'I am far too busy to talk to you, sir. I am drawing a much more interesting snail.'

Richard's interest was piqued. Amused by her quick wit, he knelt to look more closely at her work.

'It's very good,' he said. The other men had already gone into the alehouse. Richard sat down next to Mary.

He asked her about her drawing, and she blushed again. Her father often entertained artists at the rectory, but they didn't pay much attention to her. To have someone as handsome as Richard interested made her want to sing with happiness. She couldn't help noticing the long, dark eyelashes which framed his intense green eyes, and a smile that she would have been happy to see every single day.

'Are you here often?' he asked.

'I'm here most afternoons. I like it here; usually nobody notices me!'

15

'Do you always draw snails, or do you draw trees? Or people?'

'I like to draw people best, but they don't ever seem to stay still long enough!'

'Then I'll come back tomorrow and sit with you, and you can draw my likeness instead of your interesting snail!'

Mary nodded. 'I'd like that very much.'

Richard got up to go and join his friends in the alehouse and bowed theatrically as he left.

'Until we meet again, Miss…'

'Mary.'

'Mary,' he repeated.

She smiled, as she watched him walk over to the alehouse.

Today, he was later than usual. Mary waited and listened for the sound of horse's hooves. At fifteen, she knew she would be expected to marry soon, and that her father would have someone in mind, but he was far too distracted with Cromwell and the goings-on at parliament to worry about getting her wed. She had no mother to talk to about these things. She had died in childbirth when Mary was just ten years old. Her younger brother was still only five, and Mary suspected that her father may have put off making any arrangements for her own marriage until her brother was older and could take care of himself. She was in no hurry to marry, but after meeting Richard she thought that if she could marry *him*, she wouldn't mind being a wife at all. She thought it impossible though, after he boasted about his father.

He'd come to talk to her after his friends left one day, a little worse for the drink.

'He's served under two kings,' he told her, his voice full

of pride as he spoke. 'The king loves him very much. He was Groom of the Chamber, you know? He knows all the royal secrets…'

Mary had stopped sketching. She felt the gravity of his flippant admission sinking in. The man she loved must be one of the Blagges of Little Horringer Hall. His father was for the king. Her father was for Cromwell.

She decided not to mention it ever again and carried on sketching the tree. She felt as if she lived two lives. Under the willow tree with Richard, everything was perfect; while beyond its cocoon of leaves and branches the world was complicated and divided.

Richard was in high spirits when he finally arrived. He'd spent the day at Bury St Edmunds, where he had been protesting over the banning of the Maypole.

'We were shouting, "God and King Charles!" so forcefully that we frightened Fairfax and his men out of town, cowards that they are!' Richard exclaimed delightedly, trying to impress her.

'It must have been terrifying,' was the only response she could think of. The thought of her Richard being caught in the fighting worried her so much.

'I wasn't afraid' Richard puffed up his chest. 'We are on the right side. God will keep us safe.'

'How can you be so sure?'

He took her hand and kissed it. 'My darling Mary, the king is God's representative on earth, and those of us who love him have nothing to fear.'

'I don't understand why the Puritans want to stop the May dances anyway,' Mary said. 'They were such fun, and I always wanted to be the queen of May.'

'You're *my* May Queen.' Richard caressed her hand. 'And Puritans aren't exactly known for being fun. But let's not talk about such things. It will only ruin our evening.'

Later that night, as they sat under the willow tree together, and the moths danced in the moonlight that illuminated its leaves, he touched her under her dress and made her legs weak. She decided then that she didn't care about Puritans and Royalists or being the queen of May. All she could think about was the new desire that Richard had stirred in her. She didn't care about the war, or what her father would think of her choice of lover. She just wanted to be able to lay with Richard, forever, there under the willow tree.

Throughout the spring and early summer, the lovers met regularly, and the tree became their sanctuary. They talked as Mary sketched, watched the sun drop behind the trees, and then lay together in the darkness.

Some days Richard didn't arrive. Mary never asked why. Whenever her father enquired about where she had been, she told him that she had been drawing under the willow tree. He was a busy man, and although he occasionally asked to see her drawings, she kept her favourites to herself: the portraits she had sketched of Richard.

'You have a talent for portraiture,' Richard told Mary one afternoon, stroking her shoulder as they lazed behind the tree. Mary blushed, but knew he was right. She had stopped drawing birds, flowers, and snails, and now preferred to draw only him. He promised to speak to his father about marrying her, 'just as soon as the war is over.' He also vowed she would be able to draw and paint as much as she wanted when they were married and added:

'I promise to make you the happiest wife in Horringer.'

Mary had never been to Little Horringer Hall, although she had been into the village. It was much bigger than the rectory, about five miles from Barrow, and she imagined it was very grand. She daydreamed every day about being

Richard's wife and lady of the house. She still had not broached the subject of her father's alliance with Cromwell. Richard had never asked. He probably assumed that the good rector was too busy with God to become embroiled in politics. Mary thought that once the war was over, it would no longer matter whose side anybody had been on anyway.

July 1648

Richard seemed distant as they lay together under the willow tree at dusk that evening. He was picking daisies and removing their petals one by one, deep in thought.

Mary thought he was being uncharacteristically quiet.

'What troubles you?'

'Fairfax has laid siege to Colchester. My father and I have to go away to support the king's men.'

'Do you have to?' she pleaded. 'Can't you stay here with me?'

He shook his head. 'I will be back, I promise you.' He took her hand and placed the daisy he had fashioned into the shape of a ring onto her finger. 'Take this,' he said, noticing her crestfallen face. 'I promise I'll return before you even notice I'm gone, and when I do, we will tell our parents we wish to marry.'

She stroked the petals and said nothing.

'Keep your heart safe for me,' he said. 'Wear this until I return. Wait for me under our willow.'

Mary nodded, fighting back tears.

'I want to marry you more than anything in the world. I don't need the grand house, or the servants, Richard. I'd marry you if you were a pauper, I swear it.'

She clung to him, knowing that if he asked her to run away with him that night, she would gladly go.

'I love you,' he said, wiping a tear from her cheek.

'I love you too,' she replied.

They kissed, and laid in silence for a while, holding hands, neither wanting to let go. Eventually, Richard stood up, brushed the leaves from his breeches and walked slowly away without looking back, leaving Mary alone, under their tree.

On 28th August, 1648, the royalists laid down their arms in surrender to Fairfax's parliamentary troops at Colchester. All lords and gentlemen were taken as prisoners of mercy.

Every day for a month, Mary sat under the willow tree, waiting for Richard to return. The daisy ring he had put on her finger wore thin, its wispy petals falling away until all that was left was the yellow head, fading with the summer.

The leaves on the tree turned from green to yellow, then brown, and finally dropped, defeated by the winter cold. Spring brought new life, and new hope, but the lovers remained absent.

Mary was married almost four years later to Charles Beale, a kind man who encouraged her art. She would sometimes return to the willow tree to say a prayer, hoping that wherever he was, Richard knew she would never forget the summer they shared under the weeping willow.

Bury St Edmunds Wingnut Tree by Claire Holland

Having worked in Bury St Edmunds previously, I knew a perfect setting for a story inspired by trees in Suffolk. St Edmund's Abbey, once one of the most powerful, richest, and largest Benedictine monasteries in England, housed the shrine of St Edmund, the first patron saint of England. Pilgrims from all over Europe made the journey to the Shrine of St Edmund. The Abbey Gardens on Angel Hill, Bury St Edmunds is a 14-acre site where the remains of the Abbey can be found. The gardens are a place where families can enjoy the playground, visitors can explore the ruins, the pilgrim's herb garden, sensory garden, rose garden and walk along the River Lark or find a shady spot under a tree on a sunny day to relax and enjoy the tranquil surroundings. The wingnut tree can be found close to the remains of the Abbot's Garden and the hexagonal tower, now a dovecote.

Under the Wingnut Tree by Claire Holland

You told me you loved me under the wingnut tree.

July 2001

We are with friends picnicking, drinking wine, and eating sandwiches in the Abbey Gardens on a sweltering summer day. I have detached myself from the group as I am struggling to keep my true feelings hidden. I know that I do not love my boyfriend, Ed. How can I when I am constantly bombarded, every minute it seems, with thoughts of you? I am sitting propped up against the trunk of a wingnut tree, amongst the debris of a few catkins and pinnate leaves, the tree bark rough against my bare shoulders. It is scorching hot, and I am trying to keep cool by utilizing the shade provided by the massive tree. Through oversized sunglasses, I watch bees, a low buzz emitting from them, seeking nectar and pollen from the tiny flowers on the pendulous plaited green catkins hanging from the branches over my head.

Trying to generate a breeze, I fan myself with my book. Feeling giddy from the wine, I lay my book down and close my eyes, dozing. Someone approaches and, cautiously, I open one eye and am delighted to see you. I close my eye again, my breath quickening. You sit down next to me; your musky aftershave mingles with the aromatic bark of the wingnut. I feel your breath on my face, and you whisper, 'you look beautiful Clara.'

My pulse races at the feel of your warm breath on my neck. I try not to blush at the compliment, unsure what to do or say. You move closer to me and place your hand over mine, gently stroking it. Your touch is so delicate; I hardly dare breathe as I don't want you to stop.

'Clara, I need to talk to you. Can you take your sunglasses off? I want to see your eyes.'

I turn towards you and remove my sunglasses, nervous at what you are about to say.

You detach your hand from mine and run your fingers through your dark shoulder-length hair, your eyes twinkling at me, the sun catching the gold of your earrings. Stalling, you pick up a discarded catkin from the ground, turning it over in your fingers, the catkin now unable to fulfil its potential to grow into a wingnut fruit.

I can tell you are nervous, so I smile, encouraging you to talk.

'Do you want another drink?' you ask, grabbing the bottle.

As I hold out my plastic cup, my hand is shaking.

A bee flies near your face and as you move back you spill wine over me.

'I'm so sorry Clara, your dress. I'll buy you a new one.'

'It's fine, it's only white wine, it will wash out,' I tell you, reassuringly. 'What is it you want to talk to me about?'

You look even more nervous now, and instead of saying anything you take my face gently in your hands and kiss me. Tentative at first, then with urgent, unrelenting passion. I allow myself to enjoy your tongue, succumbing to you with abandon. Then, I come to my senses.

Shocked by what we are doing, I pull away.

'I'm so sorry Clara,' you begin. 'I thought that, maybe, you felt the same …'

'Tom, what do you mean?' I ask, seeking clarification. I know how I feel about you, but I'm not about to tell you, not yet. 'I want to kiss you, I really do, but what about Sarah, Ed, James, and Kelly? They could be back anytime.'

'I think I love you, Clara,' you blurt out in a rush. 'I think about you all the time, it's driving me crazy. Hardly a minute goes by when I don't think about you.'

I'm so happy I could burst. You love me. I know I love you. I have loved you from afar for months, hoping you felt the same. The looks we have given each other when we think no one else is looking. The way we both engineer to be next to each other when we go out for meals, or drinks, the theatre, with our group of friends. Because we are both in relationships with other people. Both of us unhappy in our relationships but feeling stuck and compelled to do the right thing by the other person.

'I think I love you too, Tom.'

You take me in your arms, and we kiss again, laying together under the wingnut, shaded from the worst of the high sun and its stifling heat. My gaze is drawn once more to the bees, and I watch as they feed on the intertwined catkins above our heads. We arrange to meet the following day, under the wingnut, and we doze off, helped by the extra wine we have consumed.

Awoken by the sound of someone close by, we jump apart, guilt tainting our mutual disclosure to each other. It is our friend James. He looks at us knowingly but doesn't utter a word.

Later, as we leave the park you whisper to me, 'Please, you will turn up tomorrow, won't you Clara?'

'I promise.' I whisper back.

The next day, I arrive at the wingnut tree earlier than arranged. I did not sleep well, continuously replaying the events of yesterday in my head. It is already hot. I am wearing a maxi skirt, vest top, and sandals, my hair in plaits under a floppy sun hat, and I have liberally sprayed myself with my favourite D&G perfume. I sit waiting for you, excited but apprehensive, unsure if you will show.

I see you walking towards me, and I catch my breath. You are wearing a plain white V-neck T-shirt, shorts, and trainers. You are smiling and I am relieved that you have arrived.

'Hi mate,' you say. 'I was worried you wouldn't turn up.'

'Hi mate,' I smile. 'I was worried you wouldn't turn up either.'

We wander through the Abbey Gardens, holding hands. I feel alive, you have awoken in me, thoughts, and feelings I did not know possible. As twilight nears, we stop near the remains of the Abbot's Garden wall and the hexagonal tower and kiss goodbye, the grandeur of our wingnut tree framed by the falling sun. I shiver slightly and you put your arm around me. I lead you towards the wingnut as I feel safer under its wide-spreading branches with its multiple catkins resembling strings of beads.

'What's wrong, Clara?' you ask me, concerned.

I shrug but press closer to the tree. 'I had a strange feeling that we were being watched when we were by the tower,' I tell you. 'I thought I saw someone by the tree, a woman, but I can't see her now. She seemed familiar, possibly a friend of Sarah or Kelly.'

Panicked by the thought we may have been spotted together, we agree to leave the gardens but to meet again the following week, under the wingnut, our tree. We say our goodbyes, and as you walk through the Great Gate, you turn and wave.

The following week I return to the Abbey Gardens and our tree, but you do not appear. As summer moves into autumn, the catkins of the wingnut develop into winged fruits. Faithfully, I return to the tree every week, optimistic that one day you will be there, waiting for me. Finally, I admit defeat. I have waited for you long enough; you've had your chance, and I realize that it wasn't meant to be.

I leave Ed. I move to London and get on with my life. Despite my efforts to banish the memory of you and thoughts of what could have been between us, every now and then a song, a smell, or seeing a wingnut tree will trigger a cascade of memories.

And now, here we are at a mutual friend's funeral. It's about twenty years since we last saw each other. I see you getting out of your van, while I sit in my car, trying to calm my nerves. You look smart. We've both put on a bit of weight, but it is unmistakably you, even though your dark hair is shorter now, peppered with grey and tied back.

I wait for you to walk into the church as I do not want to speak to you. I am already emotional and fear I will be unable to control what I may say to you after all these years. I take a deep breath, quickly check my reflection in the rear-view mirror before getting out of my car.

After the service, I cannot face going home. Instead, I drive to Ram Meadow Car Park, leave my car there and walk to the entrance of the Abbey Gardens on Mustow Street. I soon find myself under the wingnut tree, our tree.

In autumn, the tree has few catkins, but a plethora of winged fruit that are falling like helicopters in the gentle breeze. I sit under the tree, my eyes closed, contemplating our last meeting. Seeing you has awoken memories I had long since suppressed. I hear the crunching of leaves underfoot as someone approaches and when I open my eyes, I am surprised to see you. Before I can speak, you begin to explain what happened twenty years earlier: you say you panicked when we were spotted together, and by the time you came to your senses I had already left for London.

This time under our wingnut tree it is different. The catkins have fulfilled their destiny by evolving into winged fruits and seeds. Maybe we are like winged seeds that have a natural dormancy within them, which requires patience to overcome before, like the wingnut seed, we can germinate and grow together. We are both single, free to pursue our want of one another unabashed. You gently remove a winged fruit that has fallen into my hair, throw it aside, and we watch it slowly spin to the ground.

The Great Livermere Kissing Trees by James Brown

The trees that inspired *The Livermere Kissing Trees* stand as an isolated pair and appear destined to be together, as their trunks bend toward each other and their branches mingle. As I considered this, I remembered seeing old photographs of Victorian villagers skating on the frozen lake, and, at the same time, thought of all the Suffolk folk legends and ghost stories that contribute a sense of magic to both the village and county. I would like the resulting poem to inspire people to think about how every tree has a long history, and then treat each one with the respect that it deserves.

The trees are located near the village of Great Livermere. Begin at Church Road, near the war memorial. Follow the tree-lined lane away from the Memorial to reach St Peter's Church and enter through the white gate. Walk past the church, exiting through another white gate, and turn left onto a lane. At the end of the lane, turn right onto a large, dirt track and head towards Great Livermere Lake. After a quarter of a mile, just before reaching the lake, look to the left and you will see the 'kissing trees' on the edge of the field up ahead. Livermere Lake will be to your right.

The Livermere Kissing Trees by James Brown

Livermere is made of myth, a legendary place,
The Norman church, still thatched of roof takes centre
stage for grace.
But one legend not discovered, lost to history,
Is the tale of tragedy that made the kissing trees.

In days of old, when it was cold, the mere, it froze to glass,
And children skated on that pond, some fell, some flew, all
laughed.
One day two lovers went to try the mere as it was
snowing,
They both approached the wintry scene, and sensed
romance was growing.

They skated till they stood no more, to rest near two
young trees,
That grew beside the mere and sheltered them from bitter
breeze.
The lovers fell asleep under the trees as it grew late,
But not long after, she woke up and sought another skate.

Alas, the ice was thin when she decided to go back,
Her smile it faded gradually with every evil crack.

She tried to reach the bank, and cried *help*! 'til her throat was sore,
But her lover stayed asleep, upon the freezing floor.

When he awoke, he didn't see his love, she must have left,
Aggrieved, he packed his things and walked back cold, alone, bereft.
He went to find out why she'd gone, back to her family home,
Then her mother gently asked why he was there alone.

His panic gave his frozen legs ungodly energy,
He ran and tripped and fell his way to grim uncertainty.
Before he reached the mere, he saw a terrifying sight,
His love was lying by the trees, ethereal and white.

He laid down next to her, the frozen water everywhere,
Both their bodies shutting down, eyes in eternal stare.
When they were found, they were as one, but there was mystery,
The trees that they were under, leaning closer, plain to see.

As roots and branches mingled in the century that followed,
There were whispers of the souls that those two trees had swallowed.
But more time passed and all about the lovers was forgot,
Except for down there by the mere, forget the trees did not.

They grew together and remain there, standing tall and proud,
Powered by a love within from highest branch to ground.
The lovers' destinies entwined as one perpetually,
As long as in Great Livermere, do stand the kissing trees.

The Norton Oaks by Heather Rugg

My poem is a love story. It is a lament for the loss of countryside in large areas of England, and particularly in my local area of West Suffolk. During the pandemic, everyone stayed indoors and there was a lot of negativity and fear. In all that fear and anger, some social sites encouraged a more positive connection with the world by sharing pictures of the views from their windows. I wanted to share the view from my window: two oak trees that can be found along Ashfield Road, in Norton. They have formed the view from my window for many years. They are wonderfully ordinary trees that teem with life that stood within an old Hawthorn hedge at the edge of the lane in the village. Sadly, the hedge has now gone but they still stand as a silhouette against a backdrop of sunsets over fields and Saint Andrew's Church. I wanted to capture a sense of my relationship to the oak trees as familiar friends. I also wanted to capture the relationship they had with each other and also with the greater environment. I wanted to thank them for being there for me during the pandemic, and I wanted them to feel valued.

The Oak Lovers by Heather Rugg

They stand tall and entwined, the two lovers holding
hands over the decades.
Familiar friends that watch into my window to greet me
every morning.
Welcome friends that wait for me in the evening to soothe
me to sleep.
Calming my thoughts and lifting my spirits with their
connections to shared pasts and uncertain futures.
They stand, side by side within each other's arms tenderly
holding the sky.

Budding branches, once young and graceful, spindly, and
spreading twiglike fingers.
Keeping prickly company with the Hawthorn and Black-
thorn, baring blossoms to berries.
Shading the violets, the sweet violets and marsh marigolds
as they create a canvas of colours.
Attentively watchful of dancing insects and conducting
the musical melody of feathers.
They stand, side by side within each other's determined
arms, to reach the sky.

Now noble and venerable, diminishing in the sharing of the setting sun.
Wistful companions watched through many detached windows.
Sentimental silhouettes on an unresolved landscape of painted colours,
mechanical music and motor.
Still clinging to each other's boughs recalling dying folklore and legend.
They stand, side by side with resolute arms that reach to the sky.

MID SUFFOLK

The Hadleigh Lime Tree by Holly Turner

The tree featured in this short story is known as the common lime or the common linden, or scientifically as the *tilia x europaea*. It is a hybrid between the small-leaved and the large-leaved lime as it has features of both species of lime tree. Being a mature lime, the tree stood approximately 32m tall within St Mary's Churchyard, on the west of Hadleigh town centre and next to the Grade I listed Deanery Tower which dates back to 1495. The tree was planted in the early 19th century and features on a print of the Tower from 1823 which shows a very young tree, which is presumed to be this common lime tree.

In the summer of 2021, the tree was diagnosed with *Kretzschmaria Deusta*, also known as Brittle Cinder Fungi, and although it had still been producing a full and healthy foliage, the disease had begun in the roots and made its way up the trunk of the tree. If left untreated, the tree would have caused severe damage to the surroundings of the deanery walls and graveyard and could have caused harm to the public if its branches fell or if the tree toppled entirely. Hence the decision was made, the tree was felled, and, within the stump, the decay caused by the fungal disease is visible. What was once a treasured landmark of Hadleigh's community, representing many memories for many citizens, now stands as a stump within the church yard.

My inspiration for this short story came from a dear

friend of mine who told me about her childhood joy and her memories about this particular lime tree. When it was cut down in the summer of 2021 there was an overwhelming feeling of sadness in the town. I was inspired to make the lime tree come to life one last time. It shows how, unfortunately, each living organism – whether human or environmental – has a cycle, and the late summer of 2021 was the end of this lime tree's cycle of life.

The Little Girl and her Lime Tree by Holly Turner

To my dearest Paulette.

In 1823, the lime stood as a small yet hopeful sapling. It grew under westerly winds and selective sunspots. For two hundred years, it thrived in the grounds of the churchyard along the western edge of the small market town of Hadleigh, as its tall branches cast a shadow onto the silhouette of the deanery tower. The churchyard was an idyllic place to celebrate and mourn life in all its forms, and the lime felt joy in its world.

With a crown full of heart-shaped leafy greens covered in tufts of cream hairs and pastel yellow five-petal flowers, and his usually brown limbs that tan red in the sunshine, the lime grew to be an important figure in the community. The lime embraced the playfulness of children as he was the perfect hiding spot for all small humans. The lime epitomised the beginning of budding romances, of young lovers' first kisses, and was the ear to all prayers, sorrows, confessions, and tales. The lime witnessed many things but said nothing from his stance next to redbrick tower.

And in late February of 2021, to one little girl, the lime became her everything.

Polly visited the lime every week as she walked home from school to her grandad's cottage. He lived only a short distance from the churchyard, which allowed Polly to go see and talk to the beautiful tree. She stood closely, resting her small, soft palm against the trunk, her fingers red and nipped by the cold wind as she traced the ridged bark. The lime listened intently to all her tales.

'Hi, Mr Lime. My day was so boring today. I had maths, and I wanted to cry, but I got to sit next to Sam. You remember Sam, right? The boy I was telling you about last week, with his beautiful brown eyes. Anyways, Mr Lime, do you get cold like I do? You don't feel it, but with you being so bare and naked with no leaves, I just thought you might!' And with that, Polly put her gloves back on and then wrapped her coat-covered arms around the lime.

With the hope of warmer weather arriving soon, white bell-shaped flowers rose up around the lime's roots and shivered in the wintery light. Polly picked a few and took them to her grandad who told her they were snowdrops. He said snowdrops were a symbol of hope for better times. These tiny, early springtime flowers are also a sign of impending death. Despite their blooms of hope, death was never far behind, especially within the churchyard.

Charming and cheerful celandines would pop up and join the flowerbed later than the snowdrops. They brought an added warmth and yellow glow to the base of the lime. The tree looked down at their small golden petals and thought of Polly as a celandine flower. The lime saw the brightness pour from the girl's soul. She embodied a feeling of warmth, happiness, and pure sunshine in those early spring days.

As the spring left and the summer stretched ahead, the days were warmer, and Polly became the lime's hope and company. She sat leaning against his pale grey-brown bark reading a story about a girl who got lost in the woods and fell down a rabbit hole. Often, she wondered if the lime ever got lonely, yet she believed he never was, as he was surrounded by the afterlife-the ghosts in the graveyard that were unable to rest.

One summer's day, the sunshine disappeared, and the heavens opened as it cried tiny raindrops from the grey, miserable clouds. Usually, Polly didn't visit the lime when it rained as she would stay too long and would get too wet and too cold. Yet on this mild, rain-driven day, Polly tightly wrapped her arms around the tree and just hugged him as she softly cried.

'I'm really sorry Mr Lime. I won't be able to visit for a while as my grandad is really sick, so I won't be seeing him, either.'

As the lime heard the news, the sap leaked from his knotted burr eyes and fell onto Polly's shoulders. She continued to hug him tightly. His leaves dropped and his blossom showered around her. Polly inhaled the damp, sweet scent as she rested her head against the tree.

The wind blew as the summer rain fell heavier. Polly felt the dampened white tufts and pale-yellow flowers tumble around her. The lime was unwell too and had been suffering for many years. Disease was draining him of life. It had started in the knotwork of roots and slowly made its way up into his aching limbs. The lime was slowly decaying, and there was nothing that could be done to stop it. Just like Polly's grandad, the lime showed no improvement and was slowly dying.

At the end of August, Polly visited the lime and gasped with shock at the sight of it. The lime tree had been pollard-ed and was prematurely bare of leaves. When she reached him, she touched the lime's trunk. She thought of her grandad, now always so sleepy when she saw him, barely waking to say hello or give her a hug.

'Mr Lime,' the girl said softly. 'You remind me of my grandad. He has no hair either, and he is so sleepy too. I feel as though he's leaving us.'

She gently touched the tree's ridged bark again and noticed how it was paler than usual for this time of year.

If anything, it had always been lightly bronzed, like she became when the sun shone.

'Why have you lost your beautiful green leaves?' She asked the tree. 'You look like you've had a haircut. Your leaves never leave you until they turn brown, and the winter winds take them from you.'

Polly sat under the tree and read her adventure stories to him to cheer him up. She sat at his roots which were covered in darkening, yellow buttercups, white fairy-like dandelions, and white-petal daisies. Summer was slowly departing. A warm breeze blew freshly cut grass around the churchyard. After many stories, Polly got up to leave. She hugged the lime tightly again and asked him, 'Promise you'll be here when I come back?'

She smiled softly and stroked her hand against his paled trunk as she said her goodbyes. Polly walked away in the opposite direction of her grandad's cottage.

As she turned the corner and disappeared out of his view, the lime stood still and sad as the breeze blew. This was the last time the lime would be in her company. The last time the lime would be hugged by her. The last time the lime would hear her soft, sweet voice. The lime was soon to join the ghosts of the graveyard, as the surgeons arrived and shortly, he was felled.

On an early September morning, her grandad's burial commenced. Polly looked over to the red brick tower and noticed the lime wasn't there. She sprinted over to where the lime had once stood. Now there was nothing but a stump with a triangular darkness within, and sawdust. She sifted a pile through her fingers in the air. As the wind blew, the sawdust spiralled away from the tree stump and Polly noticed her name that she had once etched into the base of the lime's trunk as a tattoo resembling their friendship.

As her grandad's funeral continued nearby, Polly sat

beside the tree stump and witnessed the mourning of life in all its forms. Both her grandad and the lime were gone. Polly sat there on the ground in her dust-and-dirt covered black pinafore and black tights and sobbed for herself, for her grandad, and for the lime tree that had always been there for her where the snowdrops and celandines grew.

The Flatford Yew by Caroline Roberts

Flatford is a small hamlet close to East Bergholt in Suffolk.
It is a well-known landscape, immortalised in the paintings
of John Constable, who grew up there, and his presence
is everywhere it seems: in the river, the trees, and in the
buildings that remain to this day. The yew tree that stands
by Flatford Mill is solitary, its toxic leaves and branches a
threat to animals and humans; it has at times been seen as a
symbol of death. Yet the ancient yew has the ability to carry
on living even when parts of it have died, or to create and
sustain another tree within it. Its healing properties create a
tincture that is a remedy for many ailments, and in the past
half a decade the clippings from its bark have been used to
treat cancer.

Constable's story is entwined with the countryside
around Flatford, and his personal life brings an added
poignancy to the place. I read about his beloved wife, Maria
Bicknell. She and Constable were initially denied marriage
for seven years by Maria's family, who felt he was beneath
her. Ultimately, they wed, and Maria gave birth to seven
children, and had one miscarriage, in their twelve years
of marriage, the last three whilst ill with tuberculosis. The
yew's innate sense of survival and adaptation fascinates me
and made me think of Maria - who would have known
the tree - strong and fighting to stay with her husband
and to bring new life into the world. I felt that, as Maria's

health diminished, she and Constable would have held on together for as long as they could.

Slips of Yew by Caroline Roberts

My dearest, Maria. Though your body weakens, your mind I know remains strong. Rest now, the November skies beyond your window here in London are bleak and grey. Let me comfort you with talk of our beloved Suffolk.

I went down to Flatford this week gone to see my brother at the mill. There I visited the old yew tree. Do you remember, my Angel? Our yew tree, standing strong and steady on the bank between two strands of the river, it has been the source of our strength. Why can your body not be like the yew, which can restore itself, that can hold to life by the lightest of threads?

I thought of us there as if it were no more than a day ago. In those joyful weeks when we were first met. How long it has been since we were there together. Your declining health has kept us away.

I cherish those walks at Flatford in the early days of our courtship. Wandering the muddy paths that weaved their way under great oaks and elms, and through the lime-green fields of spring. The clusters of eager flowers, their delicate caps of blue and white greeting us as we passed.

We lingered at the mill pond where I had stood so many times before to observe and paint. The yew tree's curved branches were thick and lush with evergreen combs, basking in the burgeoning sun that swelled, fresh and bright, in the March sky. Its reflection expanded across the water, beyond and around us, reaching almost to the Lott's cottage on the other side.

We had walked by it so often but this time you moved closer to the yew and I held you back, afraid of its poisons.

'Take care' I urged, holding your slender hand, slight and pale, firmly in my own.

Then you calmed me, saying, 'let me tell you the truth about the yew, darling John. How it heals and renews.'

I listened, enthralled as you explained how its branches can reach down into the ground, binding them to the earth so that a new trunk grows. I held you close then, breathing in the heady scent of your hair. We whispered to one another how you were the yew tree, and I had become a part of you. Living on your love. Inseparable, as each part of the tree is from the rest, as it is from the soil, as we are. All entangled in the same earth.

You made me see things differently. The landscape that I knew so well came into sharper view, and the world became clear to me with you in it. Opening my eyes to the life and strength that the yew brings, making it forever a symbol of our love.

The yew tree welcomed me back, my Angel, as it did so many summers ago. Its waving crown bending towards me in respectful nod, aided by the thoughtful gust of an autumn wind.

Standing beneath the tree I recalled the joy of those early months together, settled in our love, and each a study of the other's heart. If only your grandfather had understood our attachment or that we could never be parted. Too small was my income as a painter. A few portraits, and the country and skies of Suffolk were not enough to support you then. How different our fortunes are now.

Our love thrived despite the restraints and the fretfulness we endured. I recalled the first summer when we met in secret by the yew. Its upturned boughs, nodding in the sultry air, seemed to beckon us to it, embracing us as an understanding mother. It sheltered us from the sun and the prying eyes of the world. Drawing us closer to one another under its shade.

Bees hummed aimlessly among the reeds, as the languid afternoon hung on the water. You lifted your tender gaze to me, stilling my sorrowful eyes with your own and soothing my fears. Reminding me that our lives were entwined always like the twisted strands of the yew's bark.

In that moment I studied your countenance. The burnished curls of chestnut hair that framed your brow and the graceful, round stroke of your cheek. Your lips, in thoughtful repose, tinted scarlet as the poppies that grow wild in the field. Your likeness, with its gentle and endearing expression, captured forever.

The memory sustains me still as I watch you fade now from my view. Your face ashen and your lips drained of all hue as you labour to speak. You have not been far from your bed for so many days.

Remember how we stole those hours together, watching the dragonflies and damselflies flit, back and forth,' busy at their short life's work around the mill pond. The yew watches them pass, as it will see you and I pass, too. Just a glimpse in its long, long life, like a sighing breath, or the tossing of a branch in the dying wind.

The time of separation seemed endless while your family forbade our marriage. The world was distorted to me then and I could hardly bring myself to paint. Nothing was in its right place save those moments with you.

Seven long years the yew kept our confidence. The secrecy and parting diminished us both. How we stood it, my dearest, only God knows.

Then bittersweet liberty as my father's death brought life to our union. His bequest of an income to me granted us the freedom to seal our love with vows.

So happy we were to marry and live together, at last, as man and wife.

And how blessed we were, my darling, so quickly and so many times over, as our dear children came to us. Each the sweet, precious fruit of our love and borne so willingly into the world. You have created so much life.

Tears brought comfort as we mourned one baby, unborn. The steadying yew listened as we grieved, weighed down by leaden clouds above. Its great head bowed sombrely in the misted air as fine beads of water fell silently, uniting with our own.

Then the hardest time of all as consumption began to draw you away. How cruel that our married years would be so shortened. Crueller still that your poor body was tested as three more children came to bear. We love the dears even so with our fullest hearts.

You told me then how the yew tree can live and thrive even while a part of it is dying. I listened with faith, so anxious to believe that the yew's strength would be your own. That your body would adapt and endure.

You are right, my Angel, that you will live on in our dear children. Their fine minds and gentle hearts are so like your own. How could I not adore them?

You inspired me once more, as you nurtured and encouraged them to new strengths and joys. And you encouraged me, too.

My heart is pained to know that Lionel, still less than a year old, will not remember you. Yet, I shall take him to

Flatford, and to the yew tree, and he will know you and your unfailing love.

Rest now my darling Maria. I will light the fire here in your room as the light fades. The winter has come early this year and the days grow swiftly shorter.

Flatford was beautiful as always when I visited. The yew remains ever green but the seasons have taken their toll. Its boughs now are brushed with a dark, yellowish hue.

Do you remember those winters? The frosted walks down from Bergholt and along the river to the mill, the water half frozen in the pond. The finches would visit us. Their tiny feathers gusted out against the cold as their hopeful song chided the dull, melancholy air.

The past five years we have taken you to warmer climes on the south coast; with its brighter, fresher air as it is supposed. I have learned to love and paint its sea and sands but have longed always for us to be where the yew stands.

Why can you not be like the yew my love, which heals and renews?

You told me, that first time, how it could fall and yet still live. That the flimsiest thread of a root can hold it to life, even restore it to health. If only its strength could be your own.

Let the slips of yew be not poison but its power to heal.

You assure me now that I will heal too. You tell me I must be strong like the yew. That we shall remain together even when you are gone.

Hold on to me my darling and let me give you life. Remember how our roots are entangled as one?

You are my whole world. You paint it and colour it. Without you it will be shaded only with grey. Stay with me a while longer and let us hold together.

Whisper to me, my Angel. Tell me once more about the yew.

The Shotley Oak by Solomon Holmes

My tree is an Oak Tree in Shotley Gate. From Ipswich town centre, follow the main road under the Orwell Bridge, then take the left fork at Freston Crossroads and follow the main road for about twenty minutes until you reach the beach. To the left is Shotley Marina, to the right, as you face the river, away from the bustle of the rarely-busy picnic benches, just above the line of beach, about half a mile down a narrow, trudged-in dirt pathway, is a staircase. This staircase faces the confluence of the River Deben and the Stour. Barely a staircase, it is more of an ascending dirt path.

Ricocheting from step to step, grasping onto a branch here, a root there, to tether yourself to safety as you heave yourself up, you are ascending now. Hands covered in dirt already, you lose your inhibitions a little and start to grasp with more confidence, allowing your hands to meld with soil.

At the top now, you are shaded from the sunshine intermittently by looming trees that sway in the gentle breeze from the river. You're encountered with more dirt paths, some less trampled than others, some barely visible through the overgrown underbrush. You pick a path and follow it. Continuing to mirror the direction of the coast to your left, walking onwards, you peek images of the river as the trees open up to present it to you. You keep on walking until you come across an outlier tree.

Thicker, more downtrodden than the rest, the tree's foundations open up and spread themselves across the dirt hill. From the vantage point of the tree, you can see down to the river below. The dirt path on which you began your journey seems insignificant below the vast expanse of the river. Looking up, there is a rope tethered to one of the many arms of the tree, stretching out towards infinity. The rope is long, and at the end of it, a makeshift seat.

I chose my tree because it often felt like a home away from home when I was growing up. My friends and I would cycle from Holbrook to Shotley Gate (An immense journey which I wouldn't dare attempt now) with nothing but a water bottle, a towel, and probably a couple of quid in our pockets, just in case the burger van was there. We'd meet other friends along the way, and we'd go swimming. The water would always be freezing - we were young and insane. We would always go up to this rope swing that hung off of a tree at the top of the cliff while we dried off. I remember laughing a lot there. I remember awkward first kisses there. I remember having juvenile arguments there.

The Rope Swing by Solomon Holmes

The rope swing was always irrelevant. So was the environment.

What mattered was the time that my father spent there, with his wife, with us, his kids.

The moments we experienced there throughout the endless summers (that have since never been as long) tethered us, like the swing, to the tree.

These moments were a gauge for every happiness to be articulated against, an insurmountable togetherness that he would look back on with a fondness that bordered on the insane.

And I did think him insane, especially when my father told me that the tree spoke to him regularly.

We were in my father's kitchen, a once prestigious affair of maternal hospitality, now an untidy room with a thin veneer of dust over everything that wasn't used on a daily basis, and a rough rusty texture to the things that were.

'What exactly has the tree been saying to you?' I asked, in my usual tone of absolute cynicism. I did not have time for magic, or nonsense, or many of the exultant things in life. I was naïve, back then.

'Everything and nothing, we have been conversing for hours at a time!' my father said. His eyes were ablaze with what I originally perceived as mania, but what was really joy. 'One forgets the content when the conversation is so riveting!' He twirled his walking stick, but barely. My Father often forgot his eighty-three years and overexerted himself, but he always managed a smile.

'So, you've been talking to a tree, for hours at a time,' I said, as I tallied up in my head the likely price of adequate care needed.

'We speak about your mother,' said my father, as if by explanation.

'Jesus, Dad!'

We looked at each other in silence. He was leaning, and lightly swaying against his stick, I could tell he wanted me to leave so that he could go talk to the tree again. I left without a word.

Even as a child I could see that my father felt a great affection for that tree. It projected a great sense of serenity onto himself and my mother, Clarissa. She would tease him when he mentioned it. She was like that: cheeky, unsentimental. Father had a sincere belief in the wisdom of the forest, in the inexorable connectedness of all things, and that humanity's fate was forever interwoven with the trees.

My mother thought it was balderdash.

I wish she could have been alive to hear the tree's voice. She wouldn't have believed it. She would rather have denied her own sanity, as would I.

There was rustling in the bushes as I waded my way through to catch my father in the act of conversing with the woodland, but I did not make myself known. Instead, I opted to hide behind a bush, *like when I was a kid*, I remember thinking. I stopped myself halfway through, pretending to be a spy, with a wrinkle of distaste at my previous childishness, but there I sat staring at my father. Listening. *Really* listening. And as I sat, I did something I hadn't done for years: I cried. I tasted the salt as tears rolled down my cheeks and brushed the corners of my lips, and I savoured that taste as I saw that my father had been right.

From the tree's highest branch there dangled a make-shift rope-swing that perpetually swirled of its own accord. My father sat on a deckchair beneath the tree, eyes closed and breathing deeply.

The tree spoke with a voice that defied logic. It came from no particular direction but undoubtedly belonged to the tree. It was unwavering, but tremulous in how it seemed to fly upon the whoosh of the wind. It was aged by the earth, gravelly but pristine with an indefinable clarity. The voice had the effect of a soft gush of wind on a summer's day, leaving goose pimples in its wake.

'You're smiling again,' said the tree, as the wind rustled the ends of its tallest branches, giving the impression of a large stretch at the end of a long day.

'You know why,' said my father in response.

'Tell me about her again.'

Father let free all of the words and passions he struggled to tell anyone else of. All of the loves, and the regrets of past decades. He beamed at the retelling, but the melancholy edge at the end of the story, the hole his beloved Clarissa left behind, amounted to a perpetual loneliness that made his waking days last an eternity.

These conversations seemed to me the only parts of my father's life where time moved as he felt time should: swiftly, and with purpose.

Father's chatter came to a stop, and the wind grew impatient. 'Have you ever been in love?' he said to the tree.

'My roots entangle themselves with countless beneath and beside me.' The tree's leaves shivered. 'The heart of the forest is within me, and I am within the heart of the forest. Through these entanglements with my fellow brothers and sisters I contribute to the communal welfare of the common wood. In this, I am in love.'

'A better a definition than any,' Father responded.

At this point, my positioning on the trampled ground became uncomfortable and I adjusted myself just a little too loudly.

'Your son is behind that tree, pretending to be a spy,' bellowed the tree.

'I know. He's not a very good one, is he?'

At this, I stood up and walked towards my father. I looked up at the tree and breathed deeply with the intent of opening my mind to the tree's embrace, but in reality, I was terrified.

'Mother would have *hated* you,' I said to the tree.

'Your father has informed me.' The tree sighed. 'He loves you deeply.'

With this, my father and I embraced once more. I felt my body language become less rigid. There was a different atmosphere to this one: it was not an embrace of sympathy like the many we'd shared since mother's death; this was an embrace of acceptance.

My hands grasped my father with such vigour that after what could have been an eternity, he had to remind me he was 'eighty-three you know,' and 'not as hardy' as he once was.

I could not stop smiling.

It's wonderful what you see when you *really* look. It's beautiful what you hear when you *really* listen.

The Ipswich Lebanese Cedar by Emily Gentry

The Lebanese Cedar in Chantry Park is better known to the people of the local Chantry housing estate as the Monkey Tree. Most of the kids - and the adults - have fallen out of the tree at some point in their lives. The tree is easy to find and difficult to miss thanks to its impressive size. To find it you need to go into the London Road pedestrian entrance of Chantry Park before heading down the main driveway directly in front of you. Then head left when the driveway branches into three directions and the tree will be just on your left past the avenue of yew trees leading down towards the old mansion. I was inspired to write about this tree because, like many people from the Chantry estate, I have fond memories of summer afternoons hanging out around the Monkey Tree and trying to climb its twisting branches. Like the experiences of the narrator in the story, I returned to the tree recently during a post Covid lockdown visit to find that it wasn't as I remembered it. This story came from the sadness I experienced in seeing something once so familiar, changed beyond recognition.

The Monkey Tree of Chantry Park by Emily Gentry

It has been a while since I last visited Chantry Park. It feels strange not to be surrounded by a group of friends excited by the prospect of the long summer's day stretching out in front of us. We used to come here often during the summer breaks of high school, before jobs and university ate away our free time. After walking through the tunnel that runs beneath the busy London Road, the main entrance is much as I remember with the long avenue of trees framing the narrow driveway disappearing off into the park. Instead of happy families carrying picnic baskets there is nothing but a cold wind scattering the leaves that have fallen to the ground.

For a moment I stand between the gateposts, lost in memories of summers I will never be able to revisit. I slowly set off across the gravel drive. The playground off to my left, usually busy with children, is silent thanks to the November chill keeping most of the parents away. My breath billows out in front of me in a white cloud and I reach up to pull my scarf a little higher. I am not here for playgrounds and, just like on those past summer days, I ignore the driveway and set off on the grass. The frost crunches beneath my feet as I walk diagonally, the tennis courts to my right and the cricket grounds to my left. Up ahead, I can just about see the mansion partially hidden behind the short avenue of yew trees that lead to the small parterre garden that my friends and I so loved playing in, when we were younger. To one side of it is a stand of trees where one in particular looms above the rest and, just like I did long ago, I find myself speeding up. For a moment I can imagine Adam goading me into a race to see who can reach our destination the quickest and I swear I can hear another set of footsteps crunching over the grass beside me. When I look over there is nobody there and my steps falter.

It is easy to forget just how big the park is. For a while I am stuck walking across an ocean of grass. Neither the trees nor the mansion appears to grow any closer. Up ahead I can just about make out the old bench, though by now it has almost crumbled away to nothing. The bench marks the edge of a steep ha-ha which has tripped more than a few unsuspecting people who expected the grass to continue. A small smile appears on my face as I remember the time Rachael forgot it was there and fell flat on her face.

Despite how much the bench has crumbled over the years it is still obvious that it was once a grand affair with the remains of intricate carvings still covering the arms and back. Two carved stone dragons stand sentinel on either side, and was once a habit of mine to pat the head of the nearest dragon before sliding down the incline. I let out a gasp when my hand encounters nothing but air, the head having long since gone. I lose my balance, sliding down onto the gravel path below.

My feet skid a little on the stony, icy path as I turn my attention to the stand of trees and the massive Lebanese Cedar standing at their heart. The Cedar has always been a favourite place to meet and hang out for the kids from the local schools. It was an old friend to many with its low hanging branches and rough bark. It was perfect for climbing, and my friends and I often raced one another to see who could climb the highest. More than a few of us still bear the scars we gained after losing our grip and falling to the hard packed needles below. I rub at my right elbow with a small wince where I had once been stabbed by a particularly sharp twig and head beneath the stone archway into the small maze beside the yew trees.

Of the two ways to reach the Monkey Tree, this was the more difficult and meant squeezing between low hanging branches of sharp needles. This way, I could easily surprise any of my friends who might have arrived before I did. The other way was via one of the park's hidden paths and wasn't half as fun. Just like before, I opt for the more difficult route but, to my surprise, there are no scratchy needles and no massive branches to climb over. It has changed since I was last here. The Monkey Tree had always been a private space with thorn bushes and low hanging branches surrounding its trunk creating a hidden clearing. On beautiful, hot August days, it could often feel like you were in your own little world. Unlike most of the other things in my life I had hoped this had stayed the same. I had, perhaps foolishly, assumed the Monkey Tree would be unchanged because of the immortality trees seem to be blessed with.

My heart sinks when I see the sight in front of me. Though the Monkey tree is still there in all its glory the low branches that snake along the ground are gone. I feel a surprising pang of sadness at their absence. My friends and I loved pretending to use them as balance beams and we'd try to push one another off them. My favourite, a branch that had intersected with a split in the trunk and was comfortable to lean against, is also gone and I walk over to lightly rest my hand against the trunk. All the branches that once made it so fun to climb are gone, cut away just like the one I loved to sit on, and the only ones remaining are too high for any child to ever reach. The clearing itself is now open to the park on all sides and winter sunlight streams through into the place that had once been dappled with shadows.

I can see the lighter bark and jagged edges where the branch was hacked down, I wish I had visited sooner when the tree was still as I remembered. I gaze at the ruin the Monkey Tree has become, and it is as though a part of my childhood has been lost.

The shock of Adam's death hits me again, just as hard as the day it happened. Though it has been at least ten years since I was in high school, I realize I had been expecting the tree to still be the same.

I sink down to the ground with a sigh, ignoring how cold the needles are beneath me, and I lean my head back against the bark close to where I used to lean all those years ago. This at least has not changed, and it feels comforting to momentarily immerse myself in a past that was once so dear to me.

I miss my friends, miss the times we used to spend here. Though still quiet and calming it doesn't feel quite the same without Adam here, telling me all about the tree. He always had such a love of nature. I should come back here again with Rachael and the others. Maybe then it would feel a little more like it used to.

'Hello, old friend. I'm sorry it took me so long to come back,' I murmur quietly, closing my eyes for a few moments.

Then I let out a sigh and stand, turning my back to the Monkey tree, gazing out across the park. I know some things cannot stay the same, but it is always disappointing when something you remember so well has gone.

The Ipswich Chestnut Tree by Francesca Mulvey

The story I am about to tell is of a chestnut tree. If you come into Christchurch Park, in Ipswich, from Westerfield Road, this tree can be found by heading down the path that leads straight ahead from the gates. Where the path forks, take the path to the right, and walk until you come to a large chestnut tree. Its wide trunk is split into pieces on one side, as though made from the pieces of other trees. Further up the tree you may also notice that part of it looks like the skull of some strange creature. This tree has stood on the land of the park longer than living memory. Something not known to many people is that it also has a few mystical tales to tell. One of the most notable of the tales is about how it came by the strange skull shape and the split in its trunk.

The Tale of a Chestnut Tree by Francesca Mulvey

Many years ago, before humans walked the earth, magical spirits inhabited the forests and open spaces of this land and Ipswich in particular. The spirits could take the shape of anything they wanted to be, from flowers and plants to trees and animals of all shapes and sizes. Many chose to become a tree or flower for a certain period, often a hundred years or so, before returning to their original spirit form and going back to the place of their origin. Some chose to become animals and remained that way for the rest of time.

There was a young spirit named Kilathon who could not decide what form he wished to take. First, he took the form of a faun, but felt uncomfortable in the uncertain, gangly body. He then attempted a hummingbird, but this did not seem to work for him either. He didn't like the pine tree shape he tried, either.

After two hundred years of trying out various shapes, from a prickly holly bush to a blue whale, the spirit became dismayed. For all the appearances he had tried, he could not find one that he liked enough to stick with. He spent much of the time that followed wandering the earth in his original, sparkling green spirit formation, miserable as he watched his fellow spirits find the forms in which they wished to spend the remainder of the earth's time.

Slowly, he developed an idea. 'If I can't choose a form to stick to, I'll just create a new one for myself!' he exclaimed and thought hard on what his favourite animal shapes had been. Of all the appearances he had tried, he had enjoyed the stag, the horse, the red kite, and the wolf the most.

'But...how to put them together, and make one amazing being?' he thought aloud, his spirit formation pulsating as he considered how best to combine the animals into one amazing being who would amaze his fellow spirits and cause wonder in the mortal creatures who walked the earth.

He mused momentarily on which animals he had enjoyed being most and decided to take on the head, torso, and front paws of a wolf, a stag's antlers, and a horse's lower body. Within a few moments, he had morphed into a combination of the three and padded and clopped his way over to a large puddle of rainwater to examine his reflection.

'I should like to travel over fields and across the seas without needing to shape a new form to do so. Red kite wings should match the colour of my skin and fur nicely, but they should be larger.'

The wings sprouted from between his shoulders, and he howled in delight. Still, something felt off. Although he liked his new form, he felt diminutive, small. He wished to be bigger. Larger than the mortal animals whose forms he had morphed into. He wanted to be something new. He grew, and grew, until he was the size of a small elephant and he felt amazing! He finally felt as though he had found his true self. The one that he knew he would spend the remainder of earth's lifespan in. He went out into the open to show off his new outer-shell to the other spirits – but their reaction surprised him. Many of them shied away, cowering in fear behind the larger animals they knew would not eat them.

Older spirits - in the forms of foxes, wolves, and some bulls - eyed him reproachfully and with much disapproval. The oldest of the spirits, a black wolf who had been on the Earth in permanent form longer than anyone's memory and acted as their leader, padded forward. There were flecks of green in his brown eyes and silver in his fur intentionally added when he had chosen to take a wolf's form.

'Kilathon, what on *earth* have you done to yourself?'

His voice boomed as he addressed this outrageous younger spirit. Kilathon bowed his new head, and had some difficulty raising it again, before addressing the Elder.

'Belnar. I have spent hundreds of years trying to find a form I took to enough to make a permanent one, but without success. I have decided to fashion myself a form out of the animals I enjoyed being the most, and so...here I am.'

Kilathon turned in a circle to proudly show himself off, even going so far as to ruffle his new feathers. A nearby red kite let out an indignant squawk at the flippant use of part of its body.

Belnar snorted. 'Kilathon, the form you have created is an abomination. You cannot be more than one animal. It goes against nature.'

'But I couldn't decide. Shouldn't I be able to take a form that makes me happy?' Kilathon's voice was pleading.

Belnar was unmoved. 'Your new form may make you happy, young one. However, it is an insult to those animals from whom you have taken parts to create your new shell.' Belnar gestured with his paw at the other animals, among whom stood or perched on the branches of trees, a great number of wolves, horses, red kites, and stags. 'Look at them. Do you not see their pain, their disapproval and disgust? Kilathon, you must choose one form and one form only. You *cannot* remain in this deformed state.'

Kilathon felt angered by this order. Belnar was not taking his own feelings into account, only those of the boring, singular animals around them. He kicked the ground with one of his back hooves, and his voice came out as a low growl, almost as deep as Belnar's. 'But I like *this* self! It makes me happy!'

'If you cannot make the decision yourself, it will be made *for* you, Kilathon! As the Elder, I have the ability to do this. Choose now, or I will choose on your behalf.'

Kilathon's hackles rose, as did his anger, as he roared, 'N*o*!'

With that, he took off at a gallop away from Belnar and the rest of the gathered animals, haring east. He could hear the angered cries, howls, and bellows of Belnar and the rest of the other animals behind him. These were followed in quick succession by the pounding of paws and hooves and the sound of flapping wings.

Kilathon was loath to try and fly. Even with their smaller wings the birds of the gathering would have no trouble bringing him down if they all worked together. Instead, he was forced to find a large enough path through the trees.

After several hours, Kilathon was finally forced to stop where Christchurch Park is now situated. His chest burned, his flanks heaved and were soaked in sweat. He looked around desperately for somewhere to hide but could see nowhere that might accommodate his large size.

Amid his growing despair, however, a new idea came to him. Using what little energy he had left, Kilathon began to build a sanctuary of bark and leaves around himself. As his new shell took shape, his existing form began to stretch and morph painfully. He cried out, realizing that he would not be able to keep hold of every part of his new body. As he morphed, he chose to keep the barest remnants of his former self.

When he had fully morphed, he stood as the chestnut tree you see today. The evidence of his pain remains in the split section of his large trunk, the girth and height of the tree mirroring the size of his previous hybrid form. That skull-like shape further up his trunk is what remains of his large wolfish head, without the antlers which had caused him such annoyance.

So he will remain, until the world itself comes to an end.

The Ipswich Hawthorn Tree by Molly Kate Britton

In folklore, hawthorn trees have long been associated with fairies, or *sidhe*. Sidhe occupy hawthorn trees, also known as fairy trees, and appear to taunt or ensnare unsuspecting humans, trapping them in their world. Folklore offers defences against the sidhe, such as iron crosses, turning clothing inside out, and obscuring your identity to prevent the sidhe from stealing it. However, often a person, once taken by the fairy tree, is gone forever.

As a child, my grandmother would tell my brother and I, stories of the fairy trees. I don't know if she believed in the fairies. I never thought to ask, though I really should have. Whether the fairies were real or not, what they represented was. Risks, hazards, things that go "bump in the night" and snatch children from their beds provide very good vehicles for putting a reasonable fear of the wild into equally wild grandchildren. It took me a while to realize they weren't stories: they were warnings.

My hawthorn tree resides in Holywell Park, Ipswich. On entering Holywell Park from the Bishop's Hill entrance, the tree will be on your immediate left. I recommend this only if you're in a particular hurry. If you have time to spare, enter Holywell Park from the main entrance, and follow the nature trail deep into the park. The path will lead you to the tree, which should not have moved from the Bishop's Hill entry point in the time it will take you to walk the longer route.

The Spirit of the Hawthorn Tree by Molly Kate Britton

'Those with ill intent are not welcome here.'

My words shatter the silence of the clearing. I stand in the shadow of the hawthorn tree, shivering in the shade. I square my jaw and strengthen my stance, and it occurs to me that I look ridiculous, bracing myself to fight a tree.

I breathe in the autumn air. Closing my eyes, the crisp chill fills my senses. In the distance church bells ring and I check the time. With any other tree, I would be shocked to find I have been here for hours already, frozen beneath the branches, but I remind myself that this is no ordinary tree. At least, not if Nan's warnings are to be believed.

The tree itself is unimpressive. Tall, as one would expect of a tree, with thin spines that end in thorns that give way to thick branches, endowed with lush green leaves and vivid red berries, much like most of the trees in this park. Yet there is something distinctly *other* about it. Something strange and intangible, an all-encompassing gravity that draws me to this tree, a force that calls out, like the air raid sirens that reverberated through my eardrums when I was a child, as my mother held my brother and I close in the shelter at the top of the garden. Before mum went missing. Before Nan disappeared. Before my brother vanished.

Every part of my body fights back as I step towards the gnarled bark, dark leaves, and crimson fruits. Nan's warnings ring in the back of my mind.

I clamber onto the knee-high root and grab onto the trunk, wrapping my arms as far around the tree as they will go. My fingers scrape against a knot in the bark and clutch at it. My legs lift and scramble until my foot catches another bump.

Slowly, as if the wood will crumble to sawdust beneath me, I move up, one knot at a time, until a craggy limb of wood is less than a meter from my face.

With one hand I reach up and grasp at the haw berries. The branch seems to pull itself away from my grasp and up, up, up, until my only option is to climb higher, higher, higher.

The first branch I grab is thick with thorns that tear my skin, and the crimson from my veins, blends with the fallen fruit on the floor.

I yank my hand away, grasping my shirt to stem the flow, and tearing pieces off until I have wrapped each palm in a layer of cloth. The haws, further than ever, gleam at me, their rosy skin glinting in the afternoon sun.

I realise with an icy feeling that the funeral will begin soon, and time is finite, as much as the hawthorn insists otherwise. My father will have woken long ago to a house even emptier than usual, full of shrines to the missing.

Today we mourn my brother, and our mother before him, and our grandmother before her, as she mourned her own mother when she was my age, only nineteen. Thinking of my father's sallow face, greeting mourners alone, spurns me to move faster.

My quest continues as I stretch for the next branch, and the next, and the next, until I feel the smooth skin of the haws against my fingers. Triumphant, I pluck them. A branch snaps. And then I'm falling.

My back hits the ground and I cough and hack until my breathing returns to normal. Another branch snaps, and I see something moving in the tree. A glimpse of leathery skin, a glimmer of black eyes. I touch my finger to the iron cross in my pocket and repeat: 'Those with ill intent are not welcome here.'

A face smirks back at me, and the voice that comes from it cracks and scrapes like a falling branch. 'But you have called for me, have you not?'

The cat-like form descends from the ancient tree, snaking down the cragged trunk. They stand tall before me, their emaciated frame looming over my own. I am analysed by eyes so dark that the light around them seems to draw in on itself, like a child sat in a corner.

'I have not called for anyone yet.'

'You have given me blood and taken fruit from my tree.'

'As an offering, not a summoning,' I respond and hold out my hand.

The thin, twig-like fingers extend, scratching against the cotton of my shirt as the fae spears the blood- soaked berries on their splintered nails and pops them in their mouth. The fruits of my labour disappear behind thin lips and sharp teeth.

'May I have your name, summoner?' they ask, holding out a hand to take mine.

'You may not *have* my name. I find that names, once given freely, are hard to replace.'

Their gentle smile becomes a smirk. 'Clever girl.'

'So they tell me.'

Their pointed ears twitch and they cock their head towards the church, at the cacophony of the bells still ringing in the distance.

'What is that infernal racket?'

'A funeral chime.' I reply, curling my lip. 'Not that there's a body to bury.'

They chuckle, a dark, low sound, like iron on flint.

'Whatever would they bury an empty casket for?'

'They're mourning'

'But you aren't.'

It's not a question. It's a statement, harsh and flat from their crimson-stained mouth.

'No sense in mourning someone who still lives.'

'You think I have your brother.'

'Yes.'

'Why do you suspect that I would want a mortal man?'

'Because I didn't say it was my brother.'

Their face contorts into a snarl, and in a low growl they state, 'You would be wise not to anger me, little girl.'

'I just want my brother back.'

'And if I refuse?'

'Then I'll make you.'

My fingers fly to my throat, grasping at the iron cross.

'You think *that* could harm me? I have survived far worse wounds than your splinter of iron could ever dream of causing. Your brother knows all about it. He learnt it when he stole from me. Didn't your grandmother teach him anything?'

'You knew her?'

'In a sense. Bothersome little girl, much like you, much like her mother before her, and her mother, too. Always approached me with her clothing on backwards, as if to confuse me. Clearly, she passed these lessons on to her descendants.' They gesture at my ripped clothing. 'She appears to have omitted a crucial detail in her little stories.'

'What would that be?'

'Something that you yourself have learned. Time passes strangely here. My minutes are your hours. He was here at May Day, stealing my flowers. Now the flowers are gone, and the haws are ripe. The winter solstice is near. If I did have your brother, there would be no telling how much time has passed for him. Too long and stealing him from me could prove fatal.'

My blade is on their throat before I register my movement, and I spit my words into their face.

'Liar!'

They smirk, a flash of sharp teeth and pitch eyes.

'It is unfortunate that your grandmother did not pass you her common sense.'

'What do you mean?'

'If you kill me, how will you get your brother back?'

I falter. They strike. I hear my name on the wind as the world fades to black.

I wake hours later in my bed, cold dark eyes filling my mind. I bolt up to a sitting position. My father is there and he pushes me roughly back into bed. Outside the window, the sun sets over the woods. I hear the church bells chime nine o'clock.

Father's voice is gruff, and his eyes are red. 'On the day we mourn your brother, you run off to play childish games and nearly get yourself killed. What were you doing climbing that tree?'

'What?'

'I found you at the foot of a tree, unconscious. What do you have to say for yourself?'

I jerk up again. 'I have to go back. I have to save him.'

My father sighs and the noise drops from his lips, landing between us, heavy as a stone.

'Your brother is dead.'

Placing his hands on the bed, he pushes himself up and to his feet, heading for the door.

'No,' I respond as he crosses the room. 'He's at the tree. The fairy has him.'

My father's shoulders tense. His grip on the door handle tightens, then releases. When he speaks, his tone is cold and brisk.

'Your brother is dead. It is selfish of you to spend the day of his funeral pretending he isn't. Your grandmother filled your head with inane stories as a child, but now you are an adult and these stories need to stop before someone is foolish enough to believe them. I lost your mother to those fairy tales, and she lost her mother to them, and now your brother is gone. I won't allow children's stories to steal any more from me.'

When he leaves, the door slams against the frame and rebounds into the wall before closing for good.

I lie down and listen as the front door opens and closes, releasing the last few mourners from my father's grief. Through the crack in my window, my name carries on the wind, and through the glass I see the rustling of the leaves in the tree, shaking in time with the call of my name.

Sitting up once more, I dress in darkness, turning my clothing inside out before pulling it on, and tiptoe to the top of the stairs, slipping past long vacant bedrooms.

My father sits in his chair in the living room, slumped and snoring, illuminated by the television set, the black and grey flickering over his sunken face.

I slink down the stairs, avoiding the creaks and cracks that lurk beneath the worn carpet. I rifle through the kitchen drawers for an iron blade, and with my cross weighing heavily on my chest, I walk towards the hawthorn tree once more.

The Ipswich Spruce Tree by Rose Dawn

The Old Cemetery off Belvedere Road, in Ipswich, opened in 1855. What makes this cemetery unique is the long driveway through its centre, leading to a magnificent spruce tree which is situated in the middle of two idyllic churches. The tree offers visitors an anchor of peace amongst the graves, and stands majestically over the driveway, welcoming all those who enter. The tree is around 167 years old, dating back to the cemetery's opening, and whilst its exact height is unknown, spruce trees can grow up to 60m tall when mature.

The two churches, although seemingly identical on first glance, were designed for different services. The church to the west of the tree is non-conformist, and is now used for storage, whereas the Anglican Church to the east, used by Father Bailey in the story, is still used as a cemetery church. The stone children are also based on a real grave, the owner of which is unknown. The grave is located not far from the tree in the Old Cemetery. 'The Stone Girls' anchors the fir tree, based upon the real-life spruce, at the centre of Father Bailey's home, supporting him even when he doubts the protection it offers him and the churchyard. Throughout Father Bailey's haunting, the fir tree is present, reminding him that of the hope it continuously offers.

I was inspired to write this story by the positioning of the spruce in the actual cemetery, which magnificently stands in the centre of the two churches overlooking the graves. The beauty of the tree in amongst a sea of loss is a reminder to all to look for the hope in the darkest moments of life.

The Stone Girls by Rose Dawn

Father Bailey sat close to the warmth of the fire, protecting himself from the cold. He could hear the wind howling through the boughs of the old fir outside that sheltered his churchyard from the brutality of the storm. He was thankful for the tree's comfort through the darkness on All Hallows Eve, especially when casting his mind back to the year prior, to the plight of the stone girls.

One year earlier

Father Bailey was resting in the church when his slumber was disturbed by a loud knocking at his door. Two workmen had arrived to deliver a new headstone. The grave belonged to two young girls, whose likeness had been immortalised in carved statues that stood proudly at the top of their stone. Father Bailey liked to observe the setting of the stone, so followed the workers towards the grave. He paused underneath the fir tree. It sheltered him from the cold breeze that descended upon the graveyard.

The fir tree stood proudly in the centre of the church-yard. Its great boughs protected the graves from the harsh elements. Father Bailey heard many stories of the great sense of hope the fir brought to visitors during their lowest moments. But since moving to the church, he had failed to grasp the hope of the tree for himself.

As the workers finished, he thanked them and headed over to the grave to admire their finished work. Father Bailey approached the grave, the presence of the stone children compelled him. As he first laid eyes on the finished stone, he heard a rumble of thunder in the distance. He closed his eyes and said a prayer over the grave. As he looked at the stone once more, one of the carved girls turned her head innocently, as if to inquire what troubled him, whilst the other laughed at the puzzled look that grew upon his face.

He rubbed his eyes in disbelief. When his gaze returned to the stone girls, they had resumed their original position. Father Bailey blamed his lack of sleep and walked away from the grave. He desired the safety of his church. But as he turned around, he spotted two small silhouettes as they ran along the branches of the fir tree.

The sound of children's laughter could be heard above the wailing of the wind. A burning sensation grew in the back of his head, and he felt as if his every move was being observed. He stumbled up the gravel drive towards the church and clutched at his ears in an attempt to escape the voices of the children pressing upon his brain.

He slammed the door, silencing the noise in his mind. Seeking solitude, he returned to the comfort of his bed, only intending to rest his eyes for a short while. But he awoke with a start many hours later. The wind had heightened during his slumber, and the low growl of thunder echoed through the eaves of the church. Fumbling in the dark for a light, he tumbled out of bed, and his matches spilt across the floor. He crawled around and searched for the lost matches. As he struggled, the sound of small footsteps could be heard as they moved across the floor. He found a rogue match and struck it. The room was unearthed from the grey of the storm. But no sooner than the light had been found it was lost again. A small breath violently extinguished its flame.

He relit the flame again and again, but to no avail. Frustrated, he continued to feel his way out of the room, when a sudden chill nipped at his fingertips. He jumped at the stony touch that grasped his hand and fell. He watched as the shadows retreated down the stairs, fleeing the scene of the crime. Hastily, he picked himself up and followed the figures, only to find no remnants of trouble as he reached the bottom of the stairs.

The front door swung open with a mighty crash, and the harsh wind of the storm hastened to invite itself in as lightning struck the fir. As the boughs were illuminated, the shadows of the stone children were revealed to be hidden amongst its branches. He watched from the doorway in horror as they began to wave, and then slowly to dance along the branch.

He ran to the tree and looked up at the shadows. Another crack of lightning struck the branch below the stone sisters. The branch broke away from the tree and fell to the ground below, barely missing him. The girls appeared to jump from branch to branch, narrowly avoiding the cracks created by the lightning.

Torn between saving the girls and protecting himself from the storm, he began to yell to the children to get down from the precarious height. His cries were lost in the wind as the shadows continued to dance around the tree.

Another spark of lighting hit directly behind one of the stone girls in the tree. A small split in the branch grew under the pressure of the girl's movement. The branch slowly began to break. He ran underneath the branch and held out his hands as it buckled under the pressure of the crack. As the branch gave way, the girl fell towards its edge just feet above his open arms.

As the stone girl hung off the edge of the branch, she looked down upon the Father. Her face emerged through the shadows, and she appeared to grin at him before letting go. He saw the shadow of the branch grow closer to his face before the world faded to black.

When he came to, he was dazed, and wondered why he lay looking up at the old fir. He was amongst a pile of debris which had fallen off the tree during the storm. He remembered the two girls and sat up. He turned to face their grave which lay untouched, the two stone children standing proudly in place just as they had been that morning.

Turning back to the fir, he saw the shadows again, who were still dancing amongst the branches. As he rubbed his eyes, he looked closer as the shadows morphed into the sprigs of the fir waving at him in the breeze.

He sighed in relief and muttered his thanks to the tree for protecting his churchyard from the eye of the storm.

He observed the dawn breaking through the branches of the trees, revealing the early rays of sun through the sprigs where the shadows once lived. He sat up and leant against the trunk of the old fir. As he cast his eyes over the churchyard, he remembered all the stories visitors had told him of the tree, and the hope that it had given them. Once Father Bailey had been reluctant to put his hope in the tree, but the old fir had offered him a second chance. Now he too would learn to anchor his hope in the fir tree, and trust that it would shelter him throughout many storms.

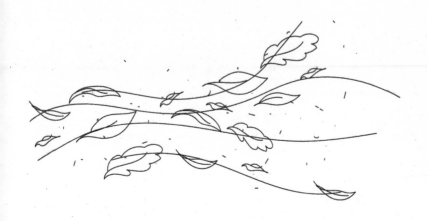

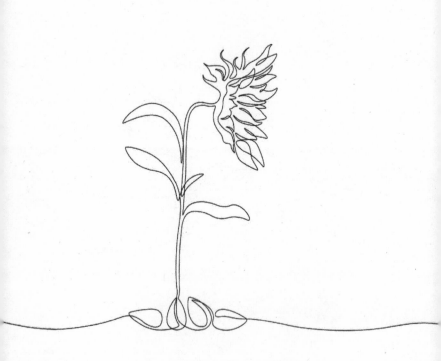

A Tree Under the Orwell Bridge by Amber Spalding

Orwell Country Park lies adjacent to the Orwell estuary, underneath the bridge that connects east and west Ipswich. The park has six pedestrian entrances and two entrances with car parks. By foot, you can start in the Ravenswood Estate, walking over the 'tump' and through the ancient Brazier Wood. Follow the footpath parallel to the A14, and the trail will take you directly underneath the bridge. To reach the tree in my poem, turn left and walk under the first archway, onto the crumbling cliffs. Hop over the small stream and continue walking until you reach the tree hunching over the coastline, half-living, half-dead, its branches snapped in the wind. Over time, two trees have grown into one, as if hugging each other for survival. It is a beautiful display of endurance.

I chose this tree not because of its twisted appearance, but because it is a survivor. I remember this tree as a child when its roots were firmly in the ground and when its leaves flourished. I grew up alongside this tree, watching as the seasons change: the flowers blossoming in spring and the leaves dropping in autumn. I have seen its branches covered in snow and watched the tide blacken its roots. The tree is the epitome of nourishment, its roots curled underneath the beach, an entangled network. My tree sustains the coastline.

A Tree Under the Orwell Bridge by Amber Spalding

where the world
seems calm and free, rests a
tree like a seed-heavy sunflower,

a tree in the shadow of civilization,
tethered as the inky tide
laps against its roots, a watermark of black

a tree whose latticed roots entwine
like a cat's cradle,
an undulating labyrinth clinging to the coastline,

a tree with its head in the sand
dissolving into the forgotten
as the river eases off its clothes,

a tree whose skin crumbles into my fingers,
falling apart with each breath,
its body imprinted on me

a tree who, when I touch it,
quivers in absence then softly
whispers for me to sit

upon the beach
curling around me as if we are one,
looking up to the concrete skies of the bridge.

EAST SUFFOLK

The Waldringfield Great Oak by Jeremy Evans

The oak tree in this story lives and breathes in the church-yard at Waldringfield. Waldringfield church is outside of the village, on a rise above the river Deben. The church is hard to spot from any distance because it is surrounded on every side by mature trees. My father was married to his second wife here, and when he died his ashes were scattered both in the river and at the base of the great oak that stands at the northern end of the churchyard. The tree marked the original boundary until new lines of graves were added in the 2000s. Just like new homes in an ancient village, the churchyard changes personality at the tree. The oak represents the last line of a time gone by.

I imagine that from the top canopy of this tree, it would be possible to see the whole length of the river Deben as well as the sloping coastal landscape that fades into the North Sea at Bawdsey.

Great Oak with You by Jeremy Evans

This is your tree story. Branch by branch, leaf to leaf, we'll tell tall tales tittle-tattling together in the breeze. Light will filter and dapple, stinging my eye as I search in the leaves for you. Some of your scorched-to-dust ashes are in the river where they have been reborn into playful seals, and some are here under this mighty oak, found in the churchyard.

There is a winding route from your tree down to the water's edge. The great oak has a view of the river; this splendid river where you and I played through my childhood and where the ripping waters come on fast-flowing spring tides and idled on lazy neaps. Some people still ask what happened in the rush of that flooding tide. Opposite is a perfectly soft and small sand beach and, behind it, woodland. It has always been a popular anchorage for little ships.

This is where we scattered your ashes on a cold and blustery April day. The ashes blew back on to me and I was glad that I could only brush the dust into the fabric of my clothes so that I could not, even if I had wanted to, remove these embedded particles of a distant you.

Some of your ash was also sited here at the earth and roots of the great oak tree. I want to hold the oak that arches over this powdered fragment, but placing my face against the grain it feels coarse and hard. It feels as if it repels me the way a body stiffens against an unwelcome embrace.

But it is your tree, the one that willows and aches in

high winds and holds its tongue with silent reserve as I talk of love and regret to the mouldy flowerpot that I forget to bring offerings to. This is your scratched earth and roots. These tufts of grass around your plaque, these dying flowers hanging in weeping browns in recycled pots are all yours, all you. They face cracks in the hard bark.

Russet-coloured leaves fall in time. Each one is a cooled life passing into the earth, warm to look at, but it is spent life. Time will re-use these leaves. The great oak discards them in the full knowledge that there shall again be new life.

On the ground, other plaques are crowding you now because you have been dead eight years and *they* must have seen how rested you are here. This sacred tree could hold any number of dead souls – I like to imagine it could hold us all under its protective canopy.

There is lichen here – the great survivor – living on the tree as well as on the dead wood of the bench; a bench that has been treated and cured to protect it from the elements, and yet the lichen can cling like a ghost to it – to anything – and make its life here in the churchyard up the hill from the river where we once sailed your wooden boats.

I never see anyone else in the graveyard but the dead. The church is barely used. On the outside, the building is warm and weathered, inside amongst the pews it is cold and damp and I do not feel welcome. Out in the church-yard, the grass grows long and when I next come it has been scythed by some unseen hands. The fallen, bleeding stalks lie on the gravestones, the smell of the cut grass fills the air with a sweet perfume.

There you lie in black dust. There, with the permanence of a seam of rock, you run through the earth from the great oak all the way down to the river's bank where you slip into water and merge with the flowing tide.

It's good to wake with your back against the rough bark of a tree even if you wake with the dead. There are children here, too.

In summer, the clover and the nettle chitter and chatter as they flutter in the breeze with a boisterous joy that to me is like small voices. The branches of the great oak sway with moody foreboding as if they will not tolerate the fuss of the wind.

I once tied two lines to a low and looping branch with a blood-red rope for the little girl at the far end of the stones. An old and very heavy piece of sawn wood made a firm, unforgiving seat. I painted it a creamy white. She tells with her eyes that she loves the colours – I say she is artistic in her ways.

The girl swings absentmindedly, thoughts on dolls or sweet puddings. Long, curled hair falls around her pale ice cream cheeks. A yellow summer dress, carelessly worn, droops from one shoulder. She has kicked off her shoes. She is singing in a low hum to her imagination and trembling leaves, blown in the cool breeze, flicker the sunlight. She sometimes has embroidery that she always drops as she departs and I put it away, or the wind does.

In winter, snow covers everything. This year it is thick and deep. The child sets about the churchyard, making snowmen and throwing snowballs on the unbroken white landscape. The oak stands stolidly, unmoved by the impossibly precarious snow drifts along each branch that perform a balancing act, with everything in perfect stasis. A deep silence covers the landscape. All other sound magically disappears.

When I next come, someone has snapped one of the red ropes and the swing hangs forlorn and listless, a broken connection.

The morning of first true spring, birds pipe songs because the sun has dramatically re-appeared and its warmth radiates again. I yearn to feel it against my skin. Winter is behind us. The grass, mossy and bright, starts to lengthen. Budding fruit trees begin to pop open into fresh leaf. White blossom of the hawthorn hedge dazzles. A woodpecker glides and dips, flapping wings sparingly as he crosses the open. The apple and pear trees have delicate pale-pink blossom the colour of a child's cheek.

The great oak lives by the cycle of sunlight. It expresses in colours: light green; dark green, yellows and autumn browns. Light defines it, energizes, and enriches it. This tree is a sculpture built by the sun.

Surrounding the churchyard, the farmer's fields are now fresh. Already, the short tufts of wheat stand proudly, quivering military spines. Below, the river is a sparkling grey-blue, glinting with white light that would blind a living eye. Below the oak, the child might dance in her silk dress and visit you with loud squeals as leaves drip with spring showers and rays of golden sunlight sparkle through spider rainbows.

You would have spoken softly and let the child come to you. You would not have told her *hush*, but smiled benignly because you knew it all passes so quickly and the time must come for all of us. There was never a need to raise your voice even as you kept an anxious eye on the turn of the tide and whilst the oak leaves fell.

And I will be lazy and lie back against the tree, my eyes closed in sunlight. The girl will sing a lullaby, picking pretty flower-heads from the stalks as she winds bare-footed in the long and wet grass. You will be the seal fishing for his supper, and I will be the one who sits up suddenly and in panic shouts, 'No!'

But it never changes the outcome.

I hear voices and so I lay back down. The first time ever I did that here, there was a thump and a scrape on top of the box because they thought they had me.

The girl is singing:
But I'll go down to the river again,
With you under a porcelain sky.
I'll go down to the river again
I'll hook a mackerel's eye.
I'll go down to the river again,
It's where we'll live and die,
I'll go down to the river again,
Where you lost you and I lost I.

When the other voices disappear, I venture into the emptied churchyard again. No-one is there, only the little girl in the summer dress and the blood-red rope dangling from the oak tree. She stares at me with a spiteful scowl; she is saying: *It's not fair.* Her singing has irritated me. After all, it was my song first, and I scowl back.

I lie down beside the tree and do not try to embrace it again. The tree does not seek human friendship. It only flutters in sunlight and stands firm in snow, mesmerized by something in the distance, up there out of reach.

I open an eye and see the girl in the pretty dress, and something about her this time makes me cry.

She lets go of the stalks of dead-headed flowers, curls her toes into the wet grass, and holding onto the edge of her pretty dress, dances in circles by our spot under your great oak tree. And the river glints back at me with silver light that dazzles as a blinding mirror on the water, reflecting me onto you.

The girl is swaying, holding the hem of her dress.

I will always sing for you when you need me to, she whispers.

Leaf-to-leaf, I softly remind you: *That's just her sweet tittle-tattle tales; you really must pay her no mind.*

The Sutton Pliocene Forest by Jordan Geller

The Pliocene Forest, near Sutton

The Pliocene Forest is but a forest in the making. At the moment, it is a collection of trees and vegetation that would have grown in East Anglia during the Pliocene epoch – a period of time that encompassed five to two and a half million years ago, before the last Ice Age. In 1977, fossil pollen grains were discovered at the site and so this conservation project was born. It can be found past Sutton Hoo (near Woodbridge) and west of Shottisham, following the footpath signs to Rockhall Wood. The discovery of the fossil grains told geologists what kind of plants grew here, and the site is a recreation of an ancient, bygone world. In a few centuries' time, the dawn redwoods planted here will dominate the Suffolk landscape with their tremendous size.

Animals exotic to our shores, such as wolves and hyenas, have had their bones discovered here. Even the teeth of the extinct Mastodons have been recovered from the site. These primordial hairy elephants, similar to the famous woolly mammoth, may have once been a common sight in Suffolk, and would have fed from these Redwoods and crimson-leaved oaks. The fossils found here of sea-shells, fish, and even whales tell us the storied and turbulent prehistory of East Anglia, and suggests the area was underwater before the Ice Age.

Millions of years later, thanks to the intervention of man, these trees can be restored to their former glory in time, even if in our short lifespans we are unable to bear witness to it. I stumbled across the Pliocene Forest on a fossil-hunting trip in the nearby Coralline Crag, and the immersive natural history of the area is what inspired this story. Though freshly planted, I see these trees as a reminder of what has come before us and what will remain after we are gone.

The Ghosts of the Pliocene by Jordan Geller

Jon was bored. The rest of his classmates didn't seem too engaged, either. Their teacher insisted on a surprise field trip, something for biology class. They ended up on the outskirts of a vast field, with only sections of small trees and bushes beyond a metal gate. The teenager whipped his new phone out once the teacher opened her mouth to speak, as Jon's attention had died a quick and painless death. He traded his teacher's enthusiastic lecture on the Pliocene Forest for a playlist of Lo-fi hip-hop beats as they set off through the fledgling forest. As the local guide spoke at great length about each and every home-grown specimen, Jon fell in line at the very back, smirking at his screen. Not a single glance was spared to any of the prehistoric flora that surrounded him.

The teacher lectured to a less-than-amused class of teenagers. 'So here we have the dawn redwood – a tree that, in a few hundred years' time, will become the tallest around. And here they are in their fledgling state.' She scanned their bright faces, but there was one whose eyes were elsewhere. 'Jon Oakmore!' the shrill teacher barked. 'Will you put that thing away? We're still on school time!'

Jon looked up with an apathetic glaze in his eye. 'I'm sorry miss, but trees just ain't my thing.'

The rest of the class murmured in agreement. Flustered beads of sweat tricked down the teacher's face. 'All right, all right! Settle down. I expect you all to pay attention – this will be on the test when we get back!'

The group set off in an orderly regiment, their groans and sighs filling the mid-morning air. Jon followed suit to the sound of muddled footsteps, his eyes never leaving his phone. Had he not been so busy signalling to the entire world how bored he was, he would have seen the branch that stretched out before him.

As soon as his forehead made contact with the wooded tendril, he gasped out in pain and dropped the phone, which fell to the sodden earth. Without pause, Jon retrieved his phone from the damp mud and found the screen cracked, as if a spider's web was sprawling upon it.

'I hope that thing isn't too badly broken.'

Jon twisted to where the ethereal voice had come from but found himself alone in the strange garden. None of his classmates or the adults were in plain sight. He pivoted his head to and fro' like an owl, back and forth, but he was met with nothing.

'I'm not boring you too much, am I?'

Wild fear etched itself into Jon's eyes as his lip wobbled. 'Who said that? Where are you?'

'I'm right here. You hit my branch. You've got to watch where you're going. Keep your eyes on the path.'

Jon stared at the miniature tree before him, perhaps only just taller than an adult man. He then circled round the tree in a panic. 'Who's there? Who said that?'

'I did. I'm here. You keep moving around me when I'm trying to talk to you. It's rather rude.'

Jon stopped when he saw no one else in the vicinity – it was just him and the burgeoning trees. 'Trees don't talk. Who's there, really?'

'The trees *do* talk. Your kind just doesn't listen.'

'*My* kind?'

'Yes, your kind. Strange little upstarts shambling about on your two roots.'

'Roots? What are you on about?'

'Do you not know your own form, fledgling? You walk upon two roots that aren't anchored to the earth, and you sprout two branches that never bloom.'

'I don't know who's really there, but this is getting pretty weird.'

'You don't have to tell me. The saplings and I were just talking about that bizarre giant that birthed a bunch of creatures like yourself. It reminded us of the times of yore.'

Jon looked behind him and saw the coach in the near distance. The tree's branch seemed to rise in its direction slightly, despite there being no wind.

'That's a bus. Everyone knows what a bus is.'

'I am a tree. I know not of this "bus" you speak of.'

The boy looked around again and saw no sign of movement. He looked again at his phone, which was definitely not working, so it couldn't be a podcast he was hearing.

'Why did the bus remind you of the times of yore?' Jon asked the tree.

'In the times of yore, this land was the forest of my ancestors. All sorts of beings walked and crept beneath our canopies. Some small, some big – like your bus creature. Some of them devoured our leaves and scraped at our bark. But we would always persevere where they would not.'

'Teacher said you were a fledgling. Have you always been as short as my stumpy old six-foot Christmas tree?'

'Short? Ha! My ancestors scraped the heavens with their canopies. I am a fledgling, true, but I retain the consciousness of my ancients. We all do, here in the forest. I even remember when we floated over to this strange land on the wind as pollen grains. We were an empire, dear fledgling. We held dominion over all, until the dark time came.'

109

Jon said nothing as the tree paused. Ten seconds went by and the boy grated his teeth waiting for his answer. 'So, what's the dark time?'

'Our roots were flooded and our trunks overcome by vast volumes of water. Our great ancestor's memories went dark, and we can see nothing more. The oaks from over the field told tales of an age of ice that followed the flood. Our trees were but husks, and what remained wasn't even fit to be food for the shaggy beasts that roamed this wasteland. Only the pines stood firm, and we don't talk about them.'

'My ancestors evolved in the Ice Age,' Jon smirked, 'and we hunted the mammoths that fed on your trees, so really you should be grateful to my kind.'

'Your kind re-planted this tree and all that surrounds us, young one. That is what we are grateful for,' the ethereal voice rasped, and its tone became more grated. 'But we are not grateful for what your kind is doing to our brothers and sisters all around this land and beyond. We hear through the roots that you chop our wood and burn our forests without giving back.'

'Well, we humans are at the top of the food chain, so what can you do?'

'Ha! Such arrogance from a sapling species. Nothing resembling your kind was even around at the height of our power. I may be young now, but I will still be here when your kind has long gone. And the empire of trees will touch the heavens once more.'

Before Jon could retort, he heard a distant shout – his teacher had finally noticed his absence. Jon looked to the tree once more. He turned to leave, but not without a final word. 'We'll see, Mr. Dawn Redwood. Maybe I'll come back when I'm old and you'll still be stumpy – or turned into a table.'

'Well met, young human. I look forward to our next

meeting. Perhaps you'll be wiser. Keep your eyes on the path, sapling, and you won't break precious things on your way.'

Before Jon could chew over these words of parting, his teacher screamed his name again. Jon spared one final glance to the budding redwood and ran off. Once the class left and the bus took off, all was silent once more in the Pliocene Forest. Centuries would pass in the blink of an eye for the Dawn Redwood, who stood as sentinels over a serene Suffolk landscape, never to be the same again.

The Butley Staverton Thicks by Alison Dudeney

Staverton Thicks, Near Butley, Suffolk

Staverton Thicks is situated near Rendlesham Forest, close to Butley, Suffolk. Rendlesham Forest is renowned for its spooky association with UFOs, but Staverton Thicks' story is more shadowy, entwined with human activity. Staverton Forest dates back to the early Middle Ages, long before the Industrial Revolution, when forestry skills were vital to making farm equipment, dwellings, and household items. Coppicing - or pollarding - harvests wood without killing the tree, but the practice leaves its mark on the way the tree grows back, altering growth patterns and shape. It is said that an oak tree takes fifty years to recover from coppicing. Staverton Thicks' ancient, coppiced oaks, no longer cut back, have continued to grow since the early days of industrialisation into weird and wonderful trees. These special, characterful trees each have their own unique history, evidenced by gnarls, knots, twists, and deformities of shape.

The Thicks has a curious atmosphere. This sense of mystery inspired me to write a story about one of these oak trees. The idea that a tree could form a special bond with two children during the years they played in it, and then call them back many years after a tragedy seemed to fit with the trees' ability to recover after coppicing.

The Sound of Silence by Alison Dudeney

Ghosts tend to avoid mirrors, but not today. In the hall's yellow light, I arrange the woollen hat, risking a glance. A shockingly pallid reflection, foreign like someone else's, stares woodenly back, revealing skin dulled with a grey tinge, the colour of gone-off white sauce. Dark rings are gathered under the eyes, panda-like. It is my first outing from the attic in fifty years. The tree is calling me, after all this time and I have to go. Out of habit, I lift thick gloves and leave the cottage.

I move into deep snow, wondering when it fell. *I'm still going*, I tell myself, turning back in through the door again. Inside, I pull long waterproof boots over warm socks, and set off again. Old habits die hard. An absence strides along beside me, nosing its presence into my empty hand and the hollow silence around me.

It's hard to know which way to go, the landscape is so altered by layers of snow, it feels as unfamiliar as my face. The fluffy whiteness in the mirror, paler than the snow now glistening under my boots, was frightening but I follow the sun through the trees and try to breathe. Cold air like water in my chest feels alien and dangerous, but I know dead people don't breathe, so I keep going.

Knuckle-bare trees reflect an amber glow, the dry snow dusting them, as if sprinkled with icing sugar. Thick-trunked, squat coppiced oaks snarled and broad-limbed, like nightwatchmen, hold themselves up, their pointing branches stark against the icy sky and reddening sun. Wary of roots, my feet ride high over the snow. I'm feeble as a strand of cotton, but I need to find that tree.

In the midst of the Thicks, steam sails into the frigid air from my mouth, just as it did, in the old days. A notion of wind touches my ear, echoing through the bare boughs, like someone whispering my name, like an otherworldly presence.

Shimmering movements catch my vision, and I spin around sharply. A herd of deer spring into view, alive with momentum, beige-spotted rumps bobbing and bouncing. Delicate, bounding hooves rustle the snow, faintly thrumming the earth beneath, infecting me with their excitement, pulling me with them beguiling me. Flying across the snow, I play a deer, threading through trees, leaping like an idiot. My heart soars as I prance then suddenly blinded, I stop. The low sun blazes through a gap in the trees, flaring like a blade into my eyes, shifting time. Back fifty years to that inky night, the twisting road, and the old Humber Hawk, its engine throbbing like rumbling thunder. The girl's warm body nestling beside me on the shiny leather bench seat, her hand resting lightly on my thigh. Thrills from her touch running up my leg. 'The Sound of Silence' plays on the car-radio, the lyrics welcoming darkness as an old friend.

The steering wheel, solid in my hands, turns, navigating another bend in the road as Blazing lights dazzle me. A lorry's honking horn blares out, mingled with Simon and Garfunkel singing the words I now struggle to remember. Something about reaching out to you...

There is a second when life hovers, just as it is. A moment before it changes forever. Before regret takes over.

The impact is violent. Before the car is crushed, I see her fly, smashing headfirst through the windscreen amid a roaring, slamming. Metal against metal. I gaze at the rod that punctures my chest, offended at how it pins me to the steering wheel. I can't get to her. I can't move. Like the song, I reach out to her, but with my heart. Darkness comes. It is an old friend.

The nightmare recedes, allowing the trees back into shadowy view. I'm heaving air, in and out, lost in a cloud of vapour, overcome with sorrow, and a brokenness that I am unable to shake off. Loss stretches out beyond me like unravelling the soul. The trees offer silent comfort which guilt does not allow me to accept.

The tree is where she broke her arm, halfway through that long, hot summer. Her courage, always foolhardy, bordered insanity. Insistent that the swing must hang from *that* branch, she clambered up with bare coltish legs, her school skirt bunched into games-knickers, a long thick plait swaying from her head and a length of rope around her neck. Heedless of my shouts that the branch would not hold her, she swung out onto its fragile length, screaming shrilly as it snapped, letting her fall the twenty feet onto the soft woodland floor. Weeks later, the tree forgave her, allowing her to tie the rope from a lower branch, even with an arm in plaster.

Gale-torn, toppled trees alter the landscape so drastically it's hard to find the oak. An inner compass guides me through the wood to another, smaller oak that I am grateful to recognise. Cracked open, hollowed out down its entire trunk, it stands like a wooden cloak spread around a dark velvety interior where we used to hide. Roots stretch out like the feet of a hat stand, visible only as humps of snow. The passing years have left it untouched. Then my eyes fall on an immense oak, broad enough to live in. A jolt runs through me, like the tree reaching out in welcome. Gnarled and knobbly from centuries of coppicing, it is without an inch of smooth bark. Sixty years ago, our hands and feet scrambled up these knobbles into stiff, reaching boughs, or to the secret letter box, a hole the size of a drawer, halfway up the trunk. This was our oak, nurturing our growth from childhood through adolescence, into young lovers. The oak we returned to for fun, for sympathy, for courage, and for love.

Hacked and cut down, time and time again over the centuries, the tree grew back with fortitude. The tree knows how to wait.

It is the anniversary of the accident today and the tree is calling me back, telling me if she is anywhere, this is where she will be.

As I glide over the snow, the gloves, boots and hat slide from my vaporous essence and I rise high into the tree, to watch the dying embers of the sunset, wrapped in the silent, ethereal chill. Here in the empty branches, I will remain till she comes. I will wait. Losing her twice would be too much to bear.

The Leiston Willow by Natasha O'Brien

I moved to Leiston, near the Suffolk coast, in 2013. To the rear of our garden was a small little park, tucked away between groups of houses. It's called Hayling's Pond. It's a great spot for a picnic, and the local angling clubs use the large, round pond there for fishing practice. In the centre of the park are two willow trees that stand side by side, and, when in bloom, dominate the landscape. Around the pond, there are a number of little decks and steps leading down to the water's edge, but you'll never find anyone swimming there. I've heard plenty of reasons why not. Most are reasonable: *good chance you'll cut yourself on whatever's at the bottom.* But some suggest that the pond is fast falling into local folklore: *there's a beast in them waters,* or, *that water's poisoned.* Whatever the case, the mystery around Hayling's Pond grew deeper when, in May 2013, hundreds of fish in the pond died overnight. Plenty of scientists came to try and solve the mystery, but no conclusions were ever made. Even now, you'll find people lounging carelessly around the water's edge, soaking in the sun which favours this small but perfectly formed local park, but you'll never find anyone dipping so much as a toe in the water. The two willow trees seem to have it right: stand back and simply admire. You never know what lurks beneath.

Willow by Natasha O'Brien

She kneels beneath the hanging branches, one hand on the bark, the other over her mouth to muffle her giggling. Like a coil wound tight, she is ready to spring. His voice echoes in the clearing, ripples across the water like a gentle breeze on midsummer morning. *Five...four...three.* She giggles again, hides behind the trunk, peeks round one last time, then tucks herself tightly behind it. *Two...one.*

'Ready or not,' he shouts. 'Here I come!'

There aren't many places to hide around the pond. A few picnic tables, if you're slight enough to disappear into the shadowy spaces under them. Sometimes they'd hide behind the cars parked on the verge. There's hardly any traffic there, but a woman came down shouting one afternoon, all waving arms and vicious spittle. She rambled about broken bones and sneered, *wait until I see your mums!* So the children tend to stay away from the cars now, especially when they know that she's watching. There's a hedge of brambles to one side of the clearing. It's tricky. There's just enough space to hide behind them without being caught by the spikes, and if you make one wrong step you could fall into the pond. Only the bravest venture there. And then there are the two willow trees, standing side by side in the centre of the clearing, next to the pond, gazing towards the water. Their tendril arms embrace and wave slowly in the warm breeze, a lumbering dance in rhythm with the soft melody of summer. Their feathery leaves whisper a faint 'hello' to those who wander in: a happy welcome, but discrete enough so that the boy next to the picnic table with his hands over his eyes can't hear the exchange.

Look closely, and you'll see the willows smiling now as Lucy giggles under her breath, waits to be found. She creeps round the trunk, staying out of view as he follows her scent, a dog on the hunt. Just as he's about to give up she jumps out at him and screams like a little monster. He jumps back, squeals loudly, and his face contorts in fear. She laughs so hard that her ribs begin to ache. He glances round to be sure no one else saw.

The sun is high now and the heat wraps around their arms and legs with suffocating, sticky embrace. It's a little cooler, though, under the willows, so they sit there together in the narrow plume of shade. He tears the leaves off a broken twig and Lucy notices that the hanging branches are dead still. If the stars were out, she'd wish for a breeze.

'Do you think we'll be married one day,' she asks him.

He scratches his ear and bats at a fly on his leg. 'Dunno. Maybe.'

'I wonder if I will marry a prince, like they do in the movies.'

'I thought you were going to marry *me*...'

She inclines her head and raises her shoulders. 'Dunno. Maybe.'

After a while, Lucy gets up and pulls at his arm, beckons him to follow. 'Come on, I have an idea!'

He hesitates to step into the sunshine and watches her from the shade. Lucy takes off her pink plimsolls and stuffs her white socks inside them. Barefoot, she edges towards the water.

'What are you doing?'

'Just dipping my feet in! Come join me!'

He steps forward. 'You can't do that! My pa says the water's poisoned!'

'Tosh!' Lucy shouts. 'Look!' She points to the gathering of lily pads in the centre of the pond. Take a microscope, and you'd see that the pads play host to a whole ecosystem of flies and other bugs: a veritable buffet for the fish that swim beneath. Just as Lucy points out, a fish leaps from the water. He sees only the final splash as the fish disappears again but knows well enough what he's witnessed.

'Think they'd be swimming round if the pond was poisoned?'

No, he thinks. They wouldn't. But he can't argue with his pa. 'Maybe it's *only* safe for the fish.'

Lucy dips her toe in. The water is cold and a slight chill washes over her as she submerges her whole foot. She takes a deep breath and puts the other foot in, too. She closes her eyes and looks upward, lets the warm sunshine linger on her face and shoulders a while as soft ripples filter out towards the pond's circular edges.

'Lucy!' His voice is desperate now. 'I mean it! Get out of there before your foot falls off!'

Eyes still closed, she can hear the whimper in his voice as he plods down the concrete steps towards her. She scrunches up her face, tightens the muscles around her eyes for only the flash of a second. She commits to memory a snapshot she hopes she'll never forget: the sensation of the cool water, the warm sunshine on her face, the gentle whisper of the willow trees.

He pulls on her arm. 'Get up! Get out of there!'

'Promise me first.'

'Promise you what?'

'That you'll marry me one day.'

He hesitates. Of course he'd marry her, but do boys say such things out loud? She threatens to submerge more of

122

her leg into the water. He watches as the waterline travels up her calf, edges towards her knee. Sweat erupts across his back.

She taunts him further and edges her bottom closer to the water. 'Or do I have to jump right in?'

'Fine!' He consents. 'I'll marry you!'

She smarts. Smiling to herself, Lucy pulls her legs out of the water and turns to find her shoes. 'I knew you would.'

It was a long, challenging winter. Toes frozen inside his boots, roads blocked with snow, tiles smashed on the drive after a night of raging gales. He's watched and he's waited, day after dreary, grey day. By April, the buds still hadn't appeared on branches, and only a few daffodils managed to break through the frozen earth. But now, in early May, the willows are finally in full bloom, and he sits in their shade as his daughter tosses a ball for their little brown dog to catch. He checks his watch: twenty to three. *Almost time.*

He'd gone up into the loft to find an old copy of the invite. The day had been a blur to him: flowers, white dresses, taffeta, and lace. *Be here for this time,* she'd said, but he forgot all the same. The vicar said, *do you,* and he wiped the sweat from his brow as Lucy's voice broke in reply. *I do.* They smiled at each other. That night, she whispered *husband* in his ear after they lay together, and the soft cadence of her voice sent tingles of pleasure across his naked body. A few months later, they sat together in the lounge, feet up after a long day at work. He laughed at a joke on the telly. She nestled in close to him, rested her hands on his shoulder and whispered again into his ear: *husband,* and then, *father.* They tasted the salt of each other's tears as they kissed, and then spent the rest of the evening trying to decide on a name. In May, they visited the park where they used to play as children. A little girl kicked and wiggled inside Lucy's outstretched belly. The tense expectation of her lingered in the air, wrapped around them with suffocating, sticky embrace. They sat together under the shade of the willow trees, laughed about the tricks they used to play on each other, and then realised that the perfect name for their child hung above them, covered them with soft shade and feathery leaves: Willow.

The first year was hard. Long nights, constant feeding, sore breasts. All the pain in the world, and still it was never enough. Year three. Emails to him at work: *I can't do this anymore.* On the phone again, he promised to try and get away early. *I'm suffocating!* She'd say. *I'm not cut out to be a mother!* He half agreed. He'd often look at Lucy and think of the things you find at upcycle shops, of old things recycled for new purposes. Things that, even with a new layer of paint, still showed their age and their intended purpose, their inability to fully adjust to the demands of a different world. Lucy had been given a hand-me-down role she could never quite squeeze herself into. She was all elbows and bony knees, in hems too short, rough wool washed too many times. But he could never tell her that. Late at night, he'd watch as she swallowed another pain pill he knew she didn't need, and he'd think to himself, she'll settle in eventually. All mothers are like this at first, aren't they?

Boxing Day. Six-year-old Willow comes to find him alone in bed.

'When's Mummy coming back?'

Half asleep still, he reaches over. The sheets are cold. One eye open, he sees the emptiness beside him, knows immediately the sting of a heart bereft. A letter on the kitchen table reads: *I need to think.* He can hardly stand and his stomach churns. *I'll be back for our anniversary.* More writing added hastily below: *if I can come back.*

He sits at the table every morning, and his coffee goes

cold as he watches the branches outside his window. He searches their bark for any sign of spring – for little green buds to burst through greyish brown skin. When they finally begin to appear, he counts down on his calendar to the twelfth of May. *Five…four…three*. Willow asks again when Mummy is coming home. *Two…one*.

Ready or not.

He opens his eyes and checks his watch again. Three o'clock. The hour they were married, seven years ago. He looks around but can only see the grass under him and the wispy, tendril arms of the great willows dancing gently in the breeze.

'Willow?'

'Over here, Daddy.'

He turns around. Willow sits at the edge of the pond, her dainty feet submerged in the water. Her pink plimsolls are placed neatly next to her, white socks stuffed inside. A hot sweat erupts across his back, and he leaps down the steps towards her.

'You can't put your feet in there! The water's poisoned!'

Willow giggles. 'Oh Daddy! It's not poisoned! Look!' She points to a black shadow darting through the water near her foot. 'It's fine for the fish!'

'Get out of there!' He reaches for her arm. 'I mean it! Before your foot falls off!'

Heaving a sigh, she pulls her legs out of the water and turns in search of her shoes.

He looks up to the road, half expects that this time she'll be there, smiling gently at the little girl who is *so* like her mother. He thinks again of the note: *If I can come back.*

Three fifteen, and no one else is at the park.

'Come on,' he says. 'Let's go home.'

As they leave, he looks back to the willow trees, and to the pond over which they stand guard. He feels a pulling deep within his chest, a mad fluttering about his heart. He fights back a few rogue tears as he opens the car door for Willow and the dog. It's just them, now, he thinks, until the day when Willow leaves him a note, too. He starts the engine and looks back one more time. Maybe that pond really *is* poisoned.

The Somerleyton Willow by Jayd Green

Where Station Road meets The Street in Somerleyton, turn left and walk past the Bowls Club, until the pond appears on the right-hand side. The willow is best seen directly opposite, from the street, but do enjoy the full length of the pond from the bench. As a writer, I have always been interested in how we use language to translate our experiences with the natural world. Part tree-study, part-dream, this story explores what we might be looking for when we habitually meet with natural objects – and what the willow might say.

* Do not go into the water. This is a work of speculative fiction, and who knows what mood the willow will be in when you visit.

Somerleyton Willow at Somerleyton Village Pond
by Jayd Green

She lays in bed, inert. She lets it hold her. When she wakes in the morning, she does not rise gracefully, like a puppet, sweeping across objects and surfaces. She lays still and swallows the taste of a night long in its passing. Her arms are folded in and her hands held together at the base of her throat. Her elbows ache with the strain of it. Some people grind their teeth in their sleep, she keeps her elbows tight like fists. The curtains are thin, so daylight crawls through, but she has taken to leaving them ajar at night anyway. In a bid to stabilize her sleep, she tries to keep the bedroom swollen with natural light.

She gets out of bed. Today she will walk – it is April and the sun shines. She thinks that by walking to the village pond daily a bond will form between her and the landscape. The willow tree becomes both a dream and an anchor. At first, she only thought the words, but once, as the sun began to set, she looked both ways to check the street was still empty. She opened her mouth, just a little, and out it spilled: *my willow*.

That night she lay in bed and when she closed her eyes she saw it again, after a moment of dreamy stillness, the willow grew tall and tempestuous, and then it swelled with anger and storm, swaying in a violent, conjured wind. The sky grew dark, and the pond water rippled. A great gust

129

blew through her clothes and skin, and the wind grabbed her shaking arms. It gripped her bones. The tree whipped from left to right, and she thought: *it is ok, it is ok, the willow does not have legs*. But the fear manifested the scene. She was seized by visions of the willow using its golden weeping branches as legs: stomping and indignant, the wordless voice of an elder god, earth quaking and windows shattering, the tree splashing into the pond and bent double and looming. Leaning down and down to her puny mortal body and then revealing to her its real, untameable face.

The next day, early in the morning, still aching with the curse of the writhing sleep she has risen from, there is a quiet tap from the white railing in front of her. A leaf caught in the mass of spider's webbing in the top right corner. When the breeze shakes the leaf, she says: *I know my error, I understand, you belong to no one but yourself* – and, without thinking – *I want to know how it feels, to be so sure.* She rubs an eye with the back of her hand. The tree is there at the distance it always was, branches gently fluttering. The morning sun turns the leaves, they flip and spin, green and gold. She watches for a time, clears her throat.

After a while, the spider comes to investigate the trapped leaf. The spider cuts it from the web and is gone, scuttling back to a gap in the join.

That night, there is moonlight, haloing the clouds and the willow. She likes the day moon better, with its ridges and pocks. So much delicate skin, and spring blue.

After that calm, dreamless night, she is passing by at early dawn when she sees the foxes: a family, gathered on the opposite bank of the pond, against the brick backdrop. They dart in and out from under the willow's skirts. She does not look at the base of the tree, for fear of knowing the willow's private connection to the ground. She knows only that the willow has it, and she does not.

The fox mother lays out on the felty lawn, legs stretched

in front and behind, paws muddy and dark. Ears twitching. Her sons and daughters yap and suckle, are sometimes nudged by a flea-bite kick of the leg. Mother flicks her tail, and it is pounced on. Mother chews her haunch, and is nearly bowled over by two sons tumbling. Mother scratches behind one ear, daughter chews the other, both lay on their bellies.

The woman sits on the pavement, gets tired of saying: *better view here* when someone points out the bench over there. Every now and then she is sniffed by a dog, who is walked by a whistling owner. She and the tree nurse aches and pains from watching the foxes when they are not hidden, hunched and unblinking.

That night, thinking of the fox mother sleeping so close to the willow, the woman throws open the curtains as wide as they will go before she gets into bed to sleep. She watches the sky, wills herself to dream, to hear the willow. Her limbs begin to feel liquid, and then she is walking to the village pond, slowly, and deliberately. The moon is full and dewy. She puts her hand up and reaches to the willow, says: *I love you; I love you, I love you.* The railing melts, and shrinks into the earth, as do the other signs of civilization.

She looks at the pond, the frogs croaking and clambering the banks, thinks the water will be cold and deeper than she expects, but as she considers stepping in, the willow's roots emerge and break the surface of the water, thick and braided together, rising to make a path to the other side of the pond. She steps onto the roots gingerly, testing their strength before committing to the watery walk. They hold steady, and steam with the heat of deep earth.

When she steps to the other side of the pond, onto the damp, velvet lawn, the fox pups sniff and nip her, yowling. The mother lifts her head, sees no threat and sleeps on.

The woman looks up at the willow, it takes up the sky

so fully, and she waits. Just looking and waiting, and she thinks the more she looks and waits, the bigger the leaves and branches become, like a head of hair thrown forward, until she cannot speak of it anymore, and they are against her skin. The leaves tickle and the branches are rough, but it is all so rooted, and the woman breathes so deep and steady that she can taste the tree and its years.

She can taste the roots it brushed against as a seed, she can taste the moment it first broke soil, she can taste its own first leaves which are long gone but still within, and she can taste the fungi and the pond which are also so much of the tree, and she can taste so much sunlight, hot and languid summer sunlight, chilled and glittering frosty sunlight, and every sunlight in between, golden autumn mud, teeming spring cells, until her tongue brushes against where the fox pups walked, and she is cradled and full and ecstatic. She has never felt so planetary.

Today she will walk. It is no longer April, the month that felt like a mountain. The white railing is back, and she sits on the pavement. A man strides past and says: *there's a bench over there you know.*

The woman smiles at the tree and the fox snout peeking out from between the golden willow's branches, rootling and snuffling something close to the ground, and says: *there's a better view here.*

The Student New Angle Prize
2022

In The Blood by James Brown
(winner of the SNAP Prize 2022)

When it came to writing a piece about East Anglia, I thought about my experiences growing up in the region. I feel deeply connected to the area both in terms of family and surroundings, and *In the Blood* explores those feelings. I am interested in the theory of genetic memory, and when it comes to identity, am curious as to how much of one's personality comes from the place they grew up in, their experiences and relationships, or if a good amount of it is already there 'in the blood.' We are all living history. Where we are or who we are with at any given time shapes not only our perception of the world, but also that of those around us. I would like *In the Blood* to inspire readers to pause, take in these moments and mindfully appreciate the history that they are part of.

In the Blood

He was proud that I stayed.

I could never be far from him of course, but as I grew older myself, I realised it was as much the infinite, Anglian skies that pulled me back when my wanderlust itched like the yellow Pyracantha we once threw down each other's school jumpers.

For weeks grandad had been living in the sitting room of their long, pink cottage that had been their home forever. The carer had lit the fire. It was warm and welcoming on that fading, autumn evening. I went to the chair that was now always by his bedside and sat. Grandad opened his eyes and smiled.

'Whatcha little 'un.'

It came as more breath than words, but his eyes sparkled, just a little. I laughed and it was genuine and surprising. I had not expected to laugh that day.

His hand floated from the bed, and I took it in mine. That delicate hand, wrapped in silk, that once felt like steel and guided me safely through Bury St Edmunds Market, while I said hello to the chickens and rabbits. That guiding arm around my shoulder, shielding me from the old men in long coats that stared beady eyed at the auctioneer, making miniscule gestures. Grandad whispered,

'Stand still or you'll buy us a horse.'

They took me to Great Yarmouth, and that time I held

Nanna's hand. Walking at the fore, Grandad opined how one did not need to go abroad to have a holiday.

'Why would I want to be anywhere else?'

How whimsical it was. He held his melting ice cream, shirt sleeves tightly rolled, craning his head to catch the drops, lest they fell on the mother of pearl buttons of his maroon, paisley waistcoat. The Pleasure Beach with all its screams and laughs was behind him, and at that moment I longed to be there. But as I sat by his bed, that fading, autumn evening, I would have given anything to be back, walking on Yarmouth seafront with Nanna and Grandad, while he told me that he didn't want to be anywhere else.

Then I remembered the cine camera nights. Flickering ghosts boating on the Broads transitioned to that everlasting couple sat proudly on the front pew of Haughley Church. She hid a crumpled tissue in her palm. The camera panned to me, standing nervously with my hands behind my back, eyes pleading to him for reassurance. The day went without a hitch. The film scratched, pitted, and finally wrapped itself around its spool. That meant it was their bedtime.

His eyes were heavy now, and as if he had been reading my thoughts, he whispered,

'Thas in the blood.'

Then he closed his eyes and slept.

Thas in the blood. Those words are my legacy, and I carry them in me. So, wherever I am, my Grandad's guiding arm is around my shoulder still, helping me to not buy a horse.

Zoe Bios by Jeremy Evans
(Runner up Prize SNAP 2022)

I was inspired by the UoS MA Creative and Critical Writing. I tried to put a little of everything I had learned about anthropocentrism, writing critically and creatively, thinking of the reader, being mindful of the responsibility of publication, all into 500 words. Hence, it is quite highfalutin but still quite heartfelt for me, a love story to critical and creative writing.

**Bios, life, as the prerogative of humans, zoe, life of all
nonhuman entities.**

A knowledge-hungry kestrel eyes a writer named Zoe
alone in a ploughed Suffolk field. Exposed in the open,
Zoe plunges her hand into one of the stilled waves of rolled
clay. An overwhelming heat of earthy knowledge scalds her.
Burned fingers are fired into pain and truth. She thrusts
deeper for she has desires. The Kestrel's head tilts as Zoe
melts slowly into the dark earth of the winter's field and is
consumed by a fungal tide that re-births her into an oak.
Alone, on uneven ground, this great oak breathes.

Suffolk sucks in wind-blown writers. Their fungal words
and idea-spores compost hotly. Exotic insects embed themselves in juicy layers of this ripe mound, inhaling its rotten,
tangy flavours, building secret warrens and tunnels. On top,
steam builds and coils in cool air spied upon by the kestrel
in soft sunlight set in a blue, ocean sky. Hungry wordsmiths
scurry for sustenance; scratching, digging, picking through
leaf and grass, burrowing for something soft and slimy to
swallow and savour.

Reading this entangled mass of parabolic foraging
as writhing writers claw the earth's depths for brave new
ideas, thought asks: *what must be explored?* Blood pours
from gaping pores on the foreheads of these contorted
authors; heads hang over keyboards, smashing against
(un-planetary) plastic to strike out some originality within

the smouldering thought chaos. *What am I trying to say?* And, *For God's sake, why am I trying to say it?*

Emotions run high as tentacular appendages crack out spasmodic words at blistering speed. Sentences rush head-first; tumbling, confused, brilliant and dull, rich, new, and unbelievable as *blah, blah, blah* slogans hit the brilliant page just daring Greta Thurnburg to insult them.

Zoe's great oak grows to be revered and, simultaneously, is despised by capitalism. Sunrise breaks big Suffolk skies to glint on machines. In Autumn, these machines strike Zoe down to second size – *bios* uprooted from *zoe*.

Winter greys the light then shocks to a cold blue. Leaves, blown in an eerie, guiltless silence, drop from emptied branches onto chocolate earth. I fancy trees were once a sentient species which, eons ago, discovered an enlightened path. Evolution turned them to saplings; saplings burst to leaf and breathed oxygen to mother earth like a child to the breast. If humankind could only metamorphose into trees and root into the earth – sharing water, communicating by chemicals, remembering who they are – *bios* could return to *zoe*.

Writers search *these* paths.

Zoe lies on the earth and stares at the infinite blue sky. Cold seeps into her shoulders from this complex mother whilst underground heat soothes from her great depths. Above, the kestrel hovers, head perfectly balanced, deciding if she may swoop down and gouge out the tongue. This way she can stem the flowing literary seam weeping from deepest East Anglian clay.

Perhaps Zoe/*zoe* will re-enter mother earth. Perhaps *bios* will acknowledge entanglement.

Lastly, body and mind stilled, the cold-eyed kestrel dips away.

The Manningtree Women by Caroline Roberts

As a woman living in Manningtree, a site of prominence in the Essex Witch Trials of 1645, I have long felt frustrated by the prominence of stories about Matthew Hopkins and other self-appointed 'witch' finders, and the absence of the women who were persecuted by them. In writing this story I hope to give a voice to at least one woman, Marian Hockett, and names to the other three women of Tendring who were hung in Manningtree. By privileging their names, and their story, I hope to redress the balance a little.

The Manningtree Witches

The air is thin and chill, and the scent of grass is carried on the breeze as it brushes, fresh, against my face. A low mist lingers on the Stour, hovering oppressively in the grey, morning light. The hem of my wool skirt is wet and heavy as it flaps at my legs, rubbing back and forth against my skin as I walk. My step quickens across the boggy earth that runs along the river.

I breathe deeply. The air is clearer here and I love to see the water.

My sister, Sarah endures her aches and ailments. When last I saw her, she complained of a new irritation and my basket now is filled with herbs and nettles for an ointment that will soothe her. I bring her comfort, as I do others who seek my help.

The thick brushes rustle, catching my ear like whispers. A solitary bee accompanies me, as if watching as I pick my way along the banks. My linen bonnet pulls at the nape of my neck and my rough fingers seek to loosen it. A strand of hair escapes.

I think of my Sarah. Always fretting, always uneasy, her mind fractious. How I wish she would walk out more and take the air, away from the filth and noise of the narrow, stifling streets.

The warning call of a magpie makes me turn but there is no one there. He flies up to the still-bare branch of a hawthorn tree and another joins him; their glossy, black plumage puffing up against the cold as they nod and chatter.

My breath is suddenly loud to me against the stagnant air. I hasten on; searching once more for the water's edge as the mist clamps down across the river.

My sister ails and I must go to her.

Then the ground shifts and I am dragged back to my fate. My basket is gone but a thick rope, heavy with mud entangles my body and tightens angrily at my throat. I am forced on towards the crossroads and up South Street towards The Green.

A crowd is gathered outside the Red Lion Inn, and they shout and jeer as two men haul me up; their coarse, eager hands groping my body as a last degradation.

I am strung alongside the other women. Only our petrified eyes console one another.

I search for my Sarah, but the truth now pricks at my mind. That in the cruellest cut she was used to convict me. Accused too of witchcraft and interrogated until she named me provider of her devil's imps. Then discarded without trial.

My own sister.

They wanted to hang me and display me with the others. To justify their fears, and their fees.

We are tied forever to this town. Our fate repeating as the myths and tales continue to label and define us.

But we have our own stories.

Me, Marian Hockett, and Anne Cooper, Helen Clarke, and Anne West.

We are the Manningtree women.

The King by Sophie Wilks

I was born in Lowestoft, so I have always loved visiting the beach. The King Triton statue was a piece I'd seen overlooking the top of the path that lined the edge of the Claremont Pier. In my writing, in 'The King' and others of my pieces, I like to concern myself with bringing Lowestoft to the surface. As a quiet landmark on the Lowestoft coast, the statue of King Triton watches over the sea, so I was inspired to write something that described Lowestoft as a place that held the potential to be magical.

The King

At twilight, I took myself for a walk. Driving to the sea-front where I knew I'd be surrounded by runners and the occasional dog walker. Lowestoft felt different here, lilac melted into soft peach where it met the charcoal grey of the ocean. Under a single angry cloud, the sea resembled a muddy pond. The artist in me itched to paint it blue, pretending I was in Greece or Italy. The sky was like syrup pooled at the bottom of a plastic cup, the milky blue-white of the day tainted with the flavours of blueberry and thick cream, the clouds appeared as froth.

This time of night felt otherworldly, so whenever the opportunity arose, I felt it was of great importance that I indulged in the delights Lowestoft had to offer.

This time of night off the Claremont Pier there was no one around unless you counted the tracksuit-ed teenagers hunched on the stone wall, smoking something I could only smell but not see. I passed them with hurried steps, falling into a rhythm of steady footfalls.

My frozen nose refreshed me in a way that hours spent at home could not. I told myself the cold would only make going home even more enjoyable.

Somehow, being alone here didn't feel quite so claustro-phobic. My trainers carved half-moons into the ochre sand, and for a moment I could pretend the passers-by wondered if I was okay. The sound of the sea felt like enough to disperse my loneliness, filling every empty orifice in my heart.

The waves rose ever so slightly, rising and rolling into a white-crested peak before collapsing onto themselves. The oceanic beast was a constantly churning organ filled with all manner of creatures. Sea birds tried their best to pierce its surface for something tangible, but none were ever rewarded.

I wandered on until I encountered my mythological friend. Set on a tall plinth, he was carved from sandy bath stone. King Triton oversaw the Turkish restaurant across the road from him, the hotels, and the doughnut stalls as far as the eye could see. I wondered what he thought of the new park.

His stony face was cast in shadow, the dusk made his weather-beaten face appear sharper. His protruding nose more prominent, his pupil-less eyes offset the shadow of his skin, smooth and ageless under the purple sky.

The sea air had eaten away at him, I just knew I was seeing him in his best light. Weather tore pockmarks into his bare chest and clawed at the cornucopia he held on so tightly to. The dolphins that surrounded him looked down forlornly at me.

I scanned the shoreline for any sign of his people. I always hoped for a glimpse of silver scales, something bigger than a normal fish with a golden fleece of hair. But all I glimpsed was the slinky mass of a seal, or possibly an abandoned bin bag.

Now, King Triton faced away from the domain he once ruled.

Salt Cellars By Rob Sadler

The initial spark for the story was two words that sound the same but are spelt differently and have different meanings – homophones. These two words were sellers and cellars. Initially I was drawn to the classic design of the condiment set, which still adorn many greasy spoon café's, pubs, and restaurant tables to this day. From thinking about the article of tableware that dispenses salt, I was then drawn to the subterranean cellars of the said public house. This led to the incident of the glass salt cellar smashing on a cellar door by means of an unknown vibrating inertia. Quite by accident, my thoughts turned to salt sellers and whether a nefarious bunch of contraband smugglers ever peddled such minerals within the actual tunnels under Ipswich? Further research into the tunnels revealed a semi-mythical network from the port (now marina) to the Spread Eagle and Woolpack pubs. The idea of locality, accuracy and reality seemed to fit together well with the competition theme of Suffolk – all I needed now was a trope and some characters to fit into 500 words!

Salt Cellars

Friday night in the Fat Cat - nubile suits sip insipid liquid and quaff at the old men swilling their dark malty dregs in the redoubtable clandestine corners of redemption. A salt cellar dances to an unknown subterranean vibration... I catch the regulars observing the vessel edging towards the precipice of the pock marked table before me. The greasy fingerprinted condiment smashes onto the cellared floor.

'They cost money you know,' grunts the surly glass collector.

Before I have time to compose a suitably sardonic quip the barman emerges from the cellar below:

'Did you hear that?' he enthuses from this submerged ladder.

'An earthquake?' I suggest.

'Must be the freight trains from the viaduct.'

I shrug, swilling the last finger of beer, and rising to my unsteady feet.

'Time, ladies and gentlemen please,' lauds the glass collector as I narrowly avoid disappearing into the cavernous hole of the cellar.

Sauntering down Spring Road in the warm balmy August night, I hear quickened footsteps behind me - they bring no threat to my beer coated contentment, until an ale- odoured hand grabs my shoulder with a panting voice.

'There's no trains this weekend so it can't be the viaduct.'

I turn to face the wide eyes of the barman.

'You won't let on about me opening the cellar door in pub hours, will you?' he enquires.

I laugh reassuringly.

'Course not.'

'The Woolie have a later licence than us – fancy a pint there?' he enthuses.

I smile and we quicken our pace to The Woolpack – he laughs of cutting through Christchurch Park in the dark, and we reminisce about the now defunct Co-Op fetes in the summers of our youth. Approaching the pub, the cellar doors are open in the street, which strikes me as odd for 23:42 at night: Two cask carrying men sporting long grey beards, innumerable tattoos and piercings greet my companion with a chiding glance.

'Wot toime d'yu call this?' growls one, in a broad Suffolk lilt.

'Yeyar, yew sid hupparst,' quips the other, his ruddy face rouge with sun and cider.

'Hush yer mouth,' quips my companion.

'This is the bloke I was telling you about.'

I follow the men into the bowels of Tuddenham Road and libations are poured freely with no small talk; trepidation hangs in the musty dank air. The same thumping and clattering that I had heard in the Fat Cat pub earlier is now … clearer – louder. A dancing light permeates from the street and flickers upon the skin art of the men.

'You have found them!' I utter in disbelief. 'The smugglers tunnels to the old docks, Alnesbourne Priory and Custom House?' I enthuse.

The beards remain silent.

'We have indeed' remarks the barman. 'The Spread Eagle and Halberd tunnels are clear of the old salt blocks and contraband, so we're excavating this one now.'

'We shan't bother with the Custom House,' laugh the beards.

A foot stamps the bolted cellar doors above us -

'Open up!'

Murmuration By Natasha O'Brien

I lost my mother a few years ago to cancer, and just before the pandemic, my husband joined me in grief when his mother was taken by that terrible disease as well. Both of these women had a profound effect on my life: they moulded me into the mother I am, and their combined memory inspires the woman I hope to yet become. When I learned that the brief for the Student New Angle Prize was to write something about Suffolk, I immediately thought of these two women: one born in Suffolk, and one who spent most of her life here. I decided to place my story in Minsmere and to write about the famous starling murmurations because my mother-in-law often visited the nature reserve in search of the starlings' great dance, and she often took my daughter there to play. I hope that readers of this story dwell not on its sadness, but on the closure that Mary finds when her sister is finally set free. I hope that they see that this is not just a story about grief, but, really, a story about love. After all, grief is simply love that doesn't know where to go anymore.

Murmuration

Mary's paddle glides through the water, and the soft whisper of ripples penetrate the almost perfect silence of the dawn. She used to come here with her sister. The quiet pools and sleepy waterways at Minsmere were their favourite place to get lost together. She looks up: shafts of feathery orange pepper the navy-blue sky as the sun lumbers from its sleep. *You'd love this,* she thinks, as she paddles through the reeds and waving grass. She looks to the front of her small craft, half expecting an answer. Her eyes rest a minute on the empty bench, and she feels that familiar pang grow deep within her chest. *It's your birthday, today,* she thinks.

Mary caught her sister dancing once. She thought the theatre empty as she placed the old CD player on the black floor and hit "play." Stepping back a few paces to the centre of the stage, she let the music fill her body while she remained in a momentary stasis. A soft, midnight sonata crept gently into her sister's lungs and filled her chest. Neck tall, arms out, but from the elbow curved gently in towards her centre of gravity. The pink satin of her shoes glittered in the spotlights as she lifted her slight weight onto the tips of her toes. And there, as if on cue, the melody took flight, and she with it. Mary watched from the shadows, careful not to let her sister see. She felt a warmth grow deep in her chest as her sister danced without reserve or judgement. For a moment, Mary wished she could become the soft chiffon dress that floated like a cloud around her sister's body; wished she could dance alongside her, limb to limb in a pretty duet. But her sister never did let anyone get too close to her, not even Mary. She often thinks of that stage now: empty and dark.

Mary reaches into the little bag next to her foot. Their father insisted on interring the ashes at the family plot, but Mary scooped some out one night before the urn was sealed in marble stone. She opens the bag and lets the grey dust filter through her fingers, drip into the soft, still water. *There,* she thinks. *Now your heart is free.*

She turns back, but her own heart is stilled as a chorus of flapping feathers erupts around her. She watches as hundreds of black starlings take flight, soar above her in formation and dance gently upon the morning breeze. The echoes of that midnight sonata play in her mind as she watches the starlings, transfixed. She thinks of her sister's chiffon dress, of the way the fabric danced with her, caressed her. Her silhouette made ethereal, like angels on Christmas cards. Mary's heart lifts, and a solitary tear glides down her cold cheek. After a moment of breath-taking adagio, the starlings settle back into the tall grasses and disappear again, as though they never were.

Writer Biographies

Alison Dudeney

After a career in leadership, sales and corporate management, Alison Dudeney is completing an MA in Creative and Critical Writing at the University of Suffolk. Interested in the human impact on the environment as well as the post-human, she writes short stories, poetry, and is currently working on a WWII novel. As a full-time writer living near Southwold, she finds inspiration in the Suffolk coast and countryside. She has published a number of poems including 'I Am String' included in 'Creative Approaches to Social Work Practice Learning.' Her poem 'Where Folktales Rise' was long-listed for the Student New Angle Prize 2021 competition. Her short story, 'The Runaway,' a 21st century adaptation of the traditional folktale, 'The Orwell Mermaid,' was published in *Suffolk Folk: East Anglian Tales for the 21st Century*, the 2021 anthology from University of Suffolk's Creative and Critical Writing MA cohort.

Amber Spalding

Amber Spalding contributed to *Suffolk Folk: East Anglian Tales for the 21st Century* in 2021 with her re-imagined folk tale 'The Witching Hour'. Her short story, 'A Good Day's Work in Lavenham,' which was shortlisted in the Student

New Angle Prize 2021 competition, also features in the collection. Amber also contributed to the 2022 "Suffolk Writes" anthology. She is currently studying for the MA in Creative and Critical Writing at the University of Suffolk. Her interests lie in exploring time through consciousness, entanglements in the Anthropocene, and Posthuman thought. She seeks to develop these interests further in her dissertation.

Caroline Roberts

Caroline Roberts is a writer and freelance theatre director based in Manningtree. She is currently studying for an MA in Creative and Critical Writing at the University of Suffolk while pursuing her interest in women's voices through short stories, contemporary, and historical fiction. She is passionate about adaptation and creative writing as a form of activism, and has just written a full-length play for performance which re-visions various folk-tale narratives. In 2021 she delivered a paper on motherhood and creative writing at the "Ill met by moonlight" conference for the Open Graves Open Minds project (University of Hertfordshire). Caroline's rewriting of the 'Malekin' folk tale was published in *Suffolk Folk* (2021), and she was recently shortlisted for the Student New Angle Prize (SNAP) for her story "The Manningtree Women".

Claire Holland

Since graduating from the University of Hertfordshire in 1999, Claire has had careers in retail, NHS administration, and Local Government. Claire started working at the University of Suffolk Students' Union in 2019. After years of dabbling in writing by attending writing retreats and courses online, Claire decided to formally pursue her passion and is currently a student at the University of Suffolk on the MA course in Creative and Critical Writing. Her reading and writing interests include all types of crime novels, particularly psychological thrillers, and she reads a wide range of authors including Agatha Christie, Ann Cleeves, Minette Walters, and Val McDermid. Claire is married with two beautiful daughters.

Dinah Cowan

After early careers in corporate travel (which allowed her to indulge in her love of exploring the world) and primary education (which allowed her to indulge in the long school holidays with her son and three step-daughters), Dinah completed a BA in Education at Anglia Ruskin University in 2013 with the intention of progressing to teacher training. She began working, however, in professional services at ARU, before moving to a role at the University of Suffolk following relocation from Essex. She is now in her final year as a student on the MA Creative and Critical Writing programme, an experience she has thoroughly relished, and which has been invaluable in giving her the confidence and discipline to write, having had a life-long passion for literature. When not reading or writing, Dinah can be found gardening, painting, and exploring new places. She hopes to never grow out of wanting to splash in muddy puddles in her bright yellow wellies.

Emily Gentry

Emily Gentry graduated with a BA in English from the University of Suffolk in 2020 and returned in 2021 to begin the MA in Creative and Critical Writing. She loves to read and write, with particular interests in fantasy, the relationship between nature and technology, and world-building. She would like to write fiction focusing on people who are under-represented in literature and is currently working on a fantasy novel featuring autistic and LGBTQIA+ characters.

Francesca Mulvey

Francesca was born in London and moved to Ipswich in 2003 where she has spent much of her life. Francesca completed a Bachelor's degree in English at the University of Suffolk in 2021, and is currently studying for a Masters in Creative and Critical Writing at the university. Francesca is autistic, and in addition to gaining a degree, she continues to overcome challenges to achieve her goals. She loves fantasy novels and can often be found writing her own fantasy/folklore-themed stories. This, along with a love for nature, helped to inform her tale for the anthology.

Heather Rugg

Heather Rugg began her career as a mental health nurse in 1995 and then moved into nursing education in 2007. Heather has always been interested in the role education plays within social justice and has been rewarded by empowering others through her role as a nurse educator. In her career, Heather worked with many service users and student nurses to achieve a sense of personal recovery and self-actualization.

Heather is inspired by the lived stories of those she has journeyed with and would like to be a voice that challenges stereotypes and develops understanding and empathy. Heather began studying for an MA in Creative and Critical Writing with the University of Suffolk to help develop the skills and attributes to enable her to tell stories and capture imaginations.

Holly Turner

Holly Turner is a post-graduate student studying for an MA in Creative and Critical Writing at the University of Suffolk, where she also recently attained a BA (Hons) in English. Being the daughter of a soldier, Holly has always struggled with connecting to a sense of place. However, she has lived in Hadleigh, Suffolk, for half her life now, and she feels it is a place that she relates to on a deeper, emotional level. Outside of her studies, Holly works in a Hadleigh café, which allows her to communicate freely with customers and listen to all the stories that reside in the place she now calls home. Academically, Holly's passions are in Gothic literature, especially the exploration of female beauty, the monstrous-feminine, and the "madwoman" trope.

James Brown

James Brown is a writer and student at the University of Suffolk. Having previously achieved a BA (Hons) in History and Ethics, he is currently studying toward an MA in Creative and Critical Writing. James specializes in poetry, lyrics, and short stories, and enjoys integrating the subjects of his degree into his writing to create thought-provoking pieces on the human condition. A keen reader of horror and science fiction, his research interests include the works of H.P. Lovecraft, existentialism, and philosophy.

Jayd Green

Jayd Green is a writer living in Norwich. She is currently a PhD student with the University of Suffolk, and editorial advisor for the experimental poetry publisher, *Osmosis Press*. Her poems have appeared in *Anthropocene*, *Foliate Oak literary magazine*, and *Royal Rose*. Forthcoming, she has a poem in the *Broken Sleep Books* eco-poetry anthology, and a duo of poems in the online literary journal *Crow and Cross Keys*. Her poem, "Dunwich Woods," won the Student New Angle Prize in 2018. Her writing and research is concerned with contemporary nature writing practices, eco-criticism, and the eco-gothic.

Jeremy Evans

Jeremy is married with two beautiful daughters. He is a keen sailor and in his spare time he writes novels, often with a sailing theme. He was longlisted for the Laxfield Prize in 2021 for his historical novel, *Dubois of the Milice*, which he hopes to publish in 2023. He is currently studying for the MA in Creative and Critical Writing at the University of Suffolk and was short listed for the University's Student New Angle Short Story Prize in 2021 and 2022. Jeremy loves stories, dogs, and ski holidays. The best day is a cold, frost-covered landscape in the shadows of long winter sunlight walking his dog towards a warm, open fire.

Jordan Geller

Jordan Geller is a student at the University of Suffolk on the MA Creative and Critical Writing program. He has lived in rural Suffolk for over twenty years and has an avid interest in palaeontology. This led to volunteering with Ipswich Museum, where he also helped to digitise and catalogue fossil collections from all over Suffolk of creatures big and small ranging from corals to mammoth teeth and woolly rhino bones. This scientific field inspires his writing, as does medieval history and fantasy. Once he has finished his Master's degree, Jordan intends to stay with the University of Suffolk to undergo a PhD in Creative Writing with a focus on fantasy manga, and hopes to one day, create his own.

Molly Kate Britton

Molly Kate Britton is a student on the MA Creative and Critical Writing program at the University of Suffolk, where she also recently completed her Bachelor's degree. Her interests lie in gothic, historical fiction. Besides writing (which she admits to having a love/hate relationship with), Molly also enjoys baking and embroidery.

Natasha O'Brien

Natasha O'Brien grew up in the United States but returned to her Suffolk roots in 2012 and has been pursuing her academic and creative writing ambitions since. She is currently studying for the MA in Creative and Critical Writing at the University of Suffolk, and in 2020 obtained a MA in Medieval and Early Modern Textual Culture from the University of East Anglia. Her creative work has appeared in *Burningword Literary Journal* and the online literary magazine, *The Write Launch*. She was also shortlisted for the Student New Angle Prize in 2022. She is currently working on her first novel, a historical fiction set in the 17th century. Natasha lives with her husband, daughter, and two dogs near the Suffolk coast.

Robert Sadler

Robert was born in Ipswich and is about to finish his second year of study for the BA in English Literature with creative writing degree. Two of his poems were published for the House and Home exhibition at the Hold in 2021, and an eco-critical piece entitled clime at change was included in the Wolsey writers Ovid metamorphosis and transformation myths project which Rob read out on BBC Radio Suffolk. His short story, 'Salt Cellars,' included here, was shortlisted for the 2022 SNAP awards. Robert is a keen actor, Instagram poet, and occasional frontman for local bands.

Rose Dawn

Rose Dawn is an avid reader and writer, and has lived in Ipswich, Suffolk her whole life. She is currently studying on the MA in Critical and Creative Writing at the University of Suffolk where she also recently obtained a BA (Hons) in English. Outside of her studies, Rose writes for the university blog *Life at Suffolk,* where she shares her passion for reading as well her love for baking tasty vegan treats. Academically, Rose's passion lies with the Brontë's, particularly their lesser-known brother Branwell, whose narrative she seeks to rewrite in future research projects.

Sarah Clark

Sarah Clark is a freelance writer and author, currently studying the MA in Creative and Critical Writing at the University of Suffolk. She has a particular interest in historical fiction, which inspired *The Rector's Daughter*, set in 17th century Suffolk, as well as her current work in progress, a novel featuring a Tudor queen. Sarah is a keen lover of history who likes to weave historical detail into her invented stories. She enjoys researching real characters from the past and giving them a voice as much as she enjoys creating new ones.

Solomon Holmes

Solomon Holmes is a postgraduate student on the MA Creative and Critical Writing programme at the University of Suffolk. He also works at the university. He is a voracious reader, an awkward talker, and a rather lazy singer/songwriter who currently writes, on average, about two songs a year. Recently, he has become more comfortable with calling himself a writer, but still cringes inwardly when speaking about it aloud. He lives with his partner in Stowmarket, Suffolk.

Sophie Wilks

Sophie Wilks is a first-year student at the University of Suffolk, studying English (with Creative Writing). After spending four years as a carer in Lowestoft, she decided to pursue her love of creative writing with the University. She was shortlisted for the SNAP writing awards in 2022 and is in the process of writing a novel and several short stories, exploring her love of the supernatural and Suffolk. She also enjoys painting and embroidery in her spare time and has recently been given the opportunity to be a content creator for the University of Suffolk.

Also Available from The University Of Suffolk Talking Shop Press

SUFFOLK FOLK:
East Anglian Folk Tales for the 21st Century.

By MA Creative and Critical Writing students.

https://www.uos.ac.uk/courses/pg/
ma-creative-and-critical-writing

In this collection of old tales re-visioned for contemporary readers, East Anglia's green children, mermaids, malekins and monsters come together with the secret lives of fairies and the power of lost-loves, making bold new stories that leap, hagstone in hand, into modern life.

"A wonderful collection of stories of Suffolk"

"A perfect gift in fact, for those with an interest in original short fiction, folk lore and Suffolk."

"If you're interested in folk tales, short stories, Suffolk, and East Anglia, then this is an ideal book to read as it encapsulates all this and more..." (Waterstones 5 star reviews)

"Folklore binds us to local landscapes, and the ties here are as insistent as ever. Shiver as you look at the witches' stone in Westleton after you have read 'The Tale of the Devil at St. Peter's Church', or take a moment to contemplate Dobbs' grave in Kesgrave Wood with 'The Tale of John Dobbs' in mind. Remember 'The Faines of Hethersett' when you stumble, bleary-eyed, from a certain pub. But the writers in this anthology do far more than show us the dark, magical, shadow side of Suffolk. Every piece reminds us that we find deep meaning in folktales precisely because they allow us to see the patterns of meaning in our own, contemporary lives" (Zoe Gilbert).

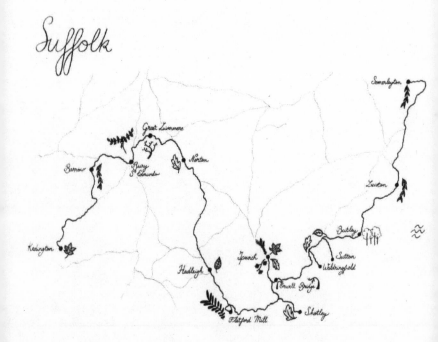

Suffolk

Somerleyton

Great Livermere

Norton

Barrow

Bury
St Edmunds

Lowton

Butley

Kedington

Ipswich

Sutton
Woodbridge

Hadleigh

Orwell Bridge

Flatford Mill

Shotley